C000148730

# Spring Harv
# PRAISE
## 2012
## DIGITAL & PRINTED SONGBOOK

**Spring Harvest**
Equipping the Church for action

**Scan to discover Spring Harvest**
What's this?

On your phone, open your barcode reader app and scan the code here. If you haven't got a barcode reader then search 'qrcode' in the app store for your smartphone.

# Copyright & Photocopying

*No part of this publication may be reproduced in any form without the permission of the copyright holder of the songs and the publisher of the songbook. Exceptions to this rule are made for holders of licences issued by Christian Copyright Licensing International, as follows:*

**CHURCH COPYRIGHT LICENCE/COLLECTIVE WORSHIP COPYRIGHT LICENCE:**

Churches, schools and organisations holding a church or collective worship copyright licence may reproduce and store the words of the songs within the terms of their licence.

**MUSIC REPRODUCTION LICENCE/COLLECTIVE WORSHIP MUSIC REPRODUCTION LICENCE:**

Churches, schools and organisations holding a music reproduction licence may photocopy the words and/or music of the songs directly from this publication within the terms of their licence.

For information about these licences visit **www.ccli.co.uk**.

**FOR UK, IRELAND AND EUROPE:**
Christian Copyright Licensing International Ltd.
Chantry House, 22 Upperton Road, Eastbourne,
East Sussex, BN21 1BF
www.ccli.co.uk

**FOR BRAZIL:**
CCLI LICENCIAMENTO DE DIREITOS AUTORAIS Ltda.
Alameda Rio Negro, 1084 - Sala 75
CEP 06454-000 Barueri, SP Brasil
www.ccli.com.br

**FOR AFRICA:**
Christian Copyright Licensing Africa (Pty) Ltd,
PO Box 2347, Durbanville 7551, South Africa
www.ccli.co.za

**FOR USA AND CANADA:**
Christian Copyright Licensing Inc,
17201 NE Sacramento Street, Portland,
Oregon, 97230 USA
www.ccli.com

**FOR ASIA PACIFIC:**
Christian Copyright Licensing International
PO Box 6644, Baulkham Hills BC,
NSW 2153 Australia
www.ccli.com.au

**KEEPING WITHIN THE LAW**

If your church musicians play direct from hymnbooks, such as this one, then the purchase price of each book pays the royalties due to copyright owners. However, if you wish to photocopy music for your musicians then you will normally need permission from the copyright owner(s). Alternatively you can obtain a Music Reproduction Licence* from CCLI which permits you to photocopy the words and music of hymns and worship songs from authorised** music publications. This licence also permits you to make customised musical arrangements for transposing instruments such as wind and brass provided the melody line remains unchanged.

* The Music Reproduction Licence is supplementary to the Church Copyright Licence, i.e. your church must hold both licences.

** An Authorised book is one which is covered by the Music Reproduction Licence. NB: Both the publication containing the song you wish to photocopy and the song itself must be covered by the Music Reproduction Licence.

For more information, contact CCLI on +44 (0)1323 436103 or visit www.ccli.co.uk.

UNAUTHORISED PHOTOCOPYING IS ILLEGAL and detrimental to the work and ministry of the songwriters and publishers.

All rights reserved. All songs are reproduced by kind permission of the copyright holders – names of which are shown below each song/hymn. Any omission of acknowledgement to composer or publisher will be corrected in future editions.

Prayers and liturgy have copyright details shown beneath them. They may be reproduced for local use with the indication of copyright, but not for resale without permission.

# Acknowledgements

Piano arrangements and music setting by David Ball
Guitar chord pages by David Ball & Becky Frith
Songbook cover design & CD-Rom artwork by Mark Prentice

Songbook internal design & layout by Ascent Creative
Printed by Halcyon
CD-Rom authored by Cambron Software

Published & distributed by Elevation, 14 Horsted Square, Uckfield, East Sussex, TN22 1QG, UK.

Part of the Memralife Group, Registered Charity number 1126997, a Company limited by guarantee, registered in England and Wales, number 6667924. Registered Office: 14 Horsted Square, Uckfield, East Sussex, TN22 1QG.

All Scriptures quotations unless indicated otherwise taken from the HOLY BIBLE, NEW INTERNATIONAL VERSION Copyright © 1973, 1978, 1984 by International Bible Society.Used by permission of Hodder & Stoughton Publishers, a member of the Hodder Headline Group. All rights reserved. "NIV" is a registered trademark of International Bible Society. UK trademark number 1448790.

Spring Harvest wishes to acknowledge and thank the following people for their help in the compilation and production of this songbook: Leigh Barnard, Vicky Beeching, Pete Broadbent, Jaqs Graham, Denise Hooper, Cheryl Jenkinson, Phil Loose, Sue Rinaldi, Dan Wheeler and Rachel Whitney.

Thank you to Marie Birkinshaw, Mark Earey and Nick Harding for liturgy contributions.

Special thanks to Brenda Cameron and all at Cambron Software for Power Music Lite and your help in developing this resource.

ISBN 978-1-899788-81-6

# Contents

**The words edition of this songbook is
available in Braille and giant print**

# Discover the Spring Harvest Digital Songbook

Over the years of the Spring Harvest songbook, there have been many helpful guest comments made which help us to refine our resource and hopefully deliver something more useful the following year. The one problem we've always struggled to solve is when a worship leader wants to play the song in a **different key to the book**. This may be because they need to sing it in a different register for male or female voice, or just drop it up or down a key to make it easier to lead. It may be that we want some songs to flow in a medley and to have them in the same key may help this to work.

Once again, we are very excited to partner with Power Music and bring you the Digital Songbook version of the Spring Harvest 2012 Songbook featuring the ability to **change the key of the guitar chords for every song**. Note that the music scores cannot be changed; maybe we'll be able to achieve this in the future!

Any of the songs can be printed out for your worship team or by utilising the software directly from a PC you can use monitor screens as "digital" music stands. You can build playlists for your church service, **search the songs by title, first line, Scripture or theme** and also ensure that everyone is playing in the same key. By going online you can see just how easy it is to use the Digital Songbook powered by Power Music Lite. We recommend though that you upgrade from within the Songbook to the full version as this enables you to add your own songs as well as create your own categories and receive future updates.

## New for 2012

Add highlights and sticky notes to the songs, just as if you were writing on a paper book!

To see the software working go to **www.springharvest.org/digisongbook** where you can see short videos to help get to grips with the software. As with all new software expect a small learning curve, but the intuitiveness of the software makes it easy to use and makes a huge difference to both worship preparation as well as 'live' worship leading.

Presently this software is Windows PC based but for Mac users we have also packaged the song scores and guitar chords as PDFs.

If you have any support issues on the programme, email Power Music on **info@cambronsoftware.co.uk**

# INSTALL

Install the
Spring Harvest
Digital Songbook
(Windows Compatible)

# UPGRADE

Upgrade to the full power of Power Music

- Add and edit your own songs
- Import from pdf
- Add your own categories
- Import/export songs
- Backup/Restore
- Receive free updates
- Save money when you
  upgrade from within
  Power Music Lite!

SINGLE LICENSE - £69
(normally £79.99)

5 USER LICENSE - £140
(normally £169.99)

10 USER LICENSE - £220
(normally £259.99)

# MAC

Scores &
chords
for Mac

# Alphabetical and Key Index

Song titles differing from first lines are in italics

7

SPRING HARVEST 2012

# CHURCH
# △CTUALLY

## GOD'S BRILLIANT IDEA

*Our hope is that this songbook will help you and your church to stay fresh and focused on the Lord as you work out his plans for your community*

**Wendy Beech-Ward**
**Director of Spring Harvest**

△9

# All the poor and powerless

Key=A

Leslie Jordan
& David Leonard

Copyright © 2011 Integrity's Praise! Music/Integrity's Alleluia! Music/Adm. by EMICMGPublishing.com, excl. UK admin. by Kingswaysongs, a division of David C Cook tym@kingsway.co.uk Used by Permission

We enjoyed recording this song for the "FRESH: New Songs for the Church" CD

Scan this QR code to hear track samples and buy the CD from EssentialChristian.com

# 2 *All you nations clap your hands*

## *(All you nations)*

Key=E

Andrew Kisumba

Strong gospel feel

**Verse**

All you na - tions clap your hands— at the name of Je - sus;

ev - 'ry tribe and ev - 'ry tongue— praise the name of Je - sus.

One day ev - 'ry knee will bow— at the name of Je - sus;

as the u - ni - verse re - sounds,— praise the name of Je - sus.— Praise—

**Chorus**

— the name——— of the Lord.——— Praise—

Copyright © 2011 Cathedral House Media/Administered by amos3music
info@amos3music.com Used by Permission

the name of the Lord. Praise his name, let ev - 'ry heart ap - plaud Christ Je - sus the ri - sen Lord. Praise With all that is with - in me, all that is with - in me, with all that is with - in me Lord I bless

*Last time to Coda*

# Prayer of approach

We meet as the family of God –
  Brothers and sisters joining with one
  purpose to love and worship the Lord.

We meet as the family of God –
  Adopted children of Abba, our Father.

We meet as the family of God –
  With Jesus as the centre, our Lord and
  Saviour, Christ.

We meet as the family of God –
  United as one by the power of the Spirit.

In love and praise we gather together today –
  We meet as the family of God.

*© 2011 Marie Birkinshaw*

# And can it be?

Key=C

Words: Charles Wesley (1707-88)
Music: Nathan Fellingham

Steadily; building

**Am7 · G/B · C · F**

1. And can it be that I should gain an in - t'rest
2. He left his Fa - ther's throne a - bove – so free, so
3. Long my im - pri - soned spi - rit lay, fast bound in
4. No con - dem - na - tion now I dread Je - sus and

R.H.

**C · F · Am7 · G/B**

in the Sav - iour's blood? Died he for me, who caused his
in - fi - nite his grace – emp - tied him - self of all but
sin and na - ture's night: thine eye dif - fused a quicken - ing
all in him is mine! A - live in him, my liv - ing

**C · F · C · D/F♯ · Gsus4 · G**

pain; for me, who him to death pur - sued? A - maz - ing
love, and bled for A - dam's help - less race. 'Tis mer - cy
ray; I woke, the dun - geon flamed with light. My chains fell
head and clothed in right - eous - ness di - vine. Bold I ap -

𝄋

**C/E · F**

love! How can it be, that thou my
all, im - mense and free; for, O my
off, my heart was free; I rose, went
proach the e - ter - nal throne and claim the

Copyright © 2011 Phat Music/Admin by Song Solutions CopyCare
www.songsolutions.org Used by Permission

God should die for me? A - maz - ing love! How can it
God, it found out me. 'Tis mer - cy all, im - mense and
forth and fol - lowed thee. My chains fell off, my heart was
crown through Christ my own. Bold I ap - proach the e - ter - nal

Last time to Coda ⊕  | 1.-3.

be, that thou my God should die for me?
free; for, O my God, it found out me.
free; I rose, went forth and fol - lowed thee.
throne and claim the crown through Christ my

4.  D.S. (v.1) al Coda

own.  A - maz - ing

⊕ Coda

me?

Great acoustic version of this one on "Fresh: New Songs for the Church"

# As I go
## (Run)

Key=C

Andy Smith

Copyright © 2011 Song Solutions Daybreak
www.songsolutions.org Used by Permission

We really enjoyed recording this one for the "Fresh: New Songs for the Church" CD →

# As we gather together

Key=D

Leigh Barnard
& Becky Frith

Steadily

1. As we ga - ther to - ge - ther   may__ our love__ in - crease;
2. As we ga - ther to - ge - ther   may__ our love__ in - crease,
3. As we ga - ther to - ge - ther   may__ our love__ in - crease;

may we ho - nour the Fa - ther   in__ the way__ that we meet.
and your grace__ and for - give - ness   be__ the goal__ that we seek.
for the sake__ of your king - dom   let__ our an - them be peace.__

Let us lift__ the name__ of Je - sus__ high__ as we__ bow low;__
May the bar - ri - ers__ of pre - fe - rence__ give way__ to love;__
May we ce - le - brate__ our dif - fe - rence__ with har - mo - ny;__

Copyright © 2011 Song Solutions Daybreak
www.songsolutions.org Used by Permission

each heart  and  mind  as  one  in  Christ,  our  voi - ces raised  in  u - ni - ty.
what Christ  a - chieved  e - ter - nal - ly,  may  we  re - flect  in  u - ni - ty.
one  song,  one  church,  one God  on  high,  for - e - ver  we  will  wor - ship you.

A          Dsus4/A D/A      G2              A

*1.*                                               *D.C. (v.2)*
D        Em7        D/F#        Em/G        D        Em7        D/F#        Em/G

*2.,3.*
G/B  *Chorus*            A/C#                    D/F#

Though  we   are  ma - ny,  we  wor  -  ship  one  God;

G                    A                    D

joined  by  the  Spi - rit,  we  ho  -  nour  you, Lord.

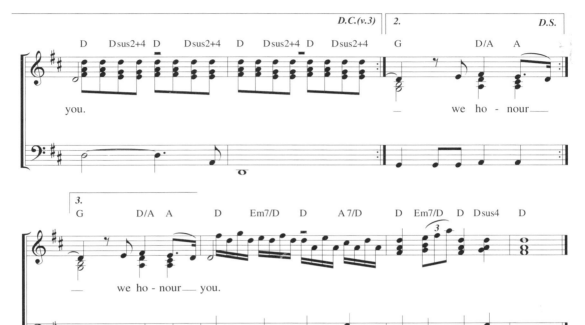

# Spring Harvest,
## Apptually.

The Spring Harvest iPhone App
Available now in the App Store

Also available for Android and BlackBerry

# 6

# At your name

Key=A

Tim Hughes
& Phil Wickham

With strength

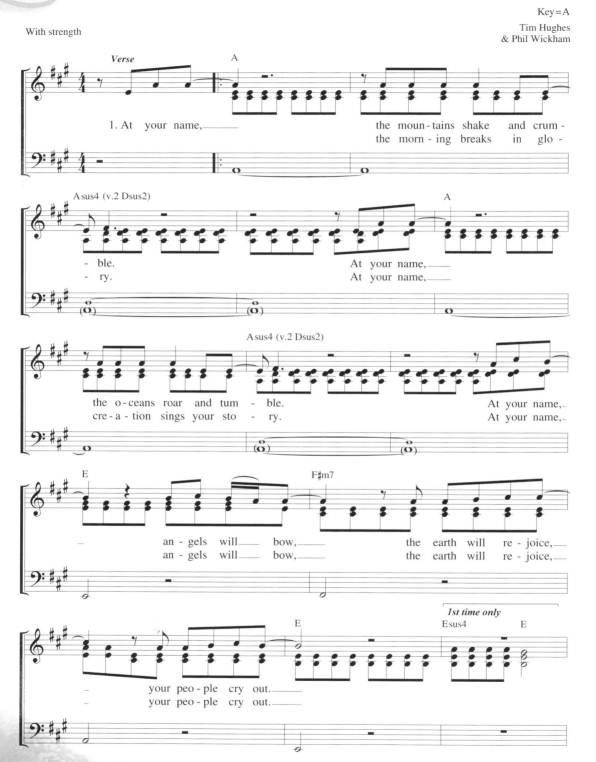

*Verse*

1. At your name,_____ the moun-tains shake and crum-
   the morn-ing breaks in glo-

- ble.
- ry.

At your name,_____
At your name,_____

the o-ceans roar and tum - ble.
cre-a-tion sings your sto - ry.

At your name,_
At your name,_

an - gels will___ bow,_____ the earth will re - joice,_____
an - gels will___ bow,_____ the earth will re - joice,_____

*1st time only*

your peo - ple cry out._____
your peo - ple cry out._____

Copyright © 2011 Thankyou Music/Adm. by worshiptogether.com Songs excl. UK & Europe, adm. by Kingswaysongs, a division of David C Cook tym@kingsway.co.uk & Phil Wickham Music/Seems Like Music/Simpleville Music/Small Stone Media/ Song Solutions Daybreak www.songsolutions.org Used by Permission

*Chorus*

Lord of all the earth,— we'll shout your name, shout your name,

fill-ing up the skies— with end-less praise,— end-less praise.

Yah-weh, Yah-weh,— we love to shout your name,— O— Lord.—

**1.,4.**

*Last time to Coda*

*D.C. (v.2)*

2. At your name,—

**3.**

*D.S. al Coda*

**2.**

*Mid section*

There is

# 7

# Be lifted high

Key=B♭

Capo 3 (Em)

Brian Johnson, Christa Black Gifford
& Tim Hughes

Gradually building

Be lift-ed____ high, be lift-ed____ high; for your

glo - ry, be lift-ed high.____ Be lift-ed____ high, be lift-ed____

high; for your glo - ry, be lift-ed high.____ Be lift-ed____

1. You're the King of all the a - ges,
2. You're the e - ver - last - ing Fa - ther,

you're the Au - thor of sal - va - tion, you're the rea - son why we're sing-ing
you're the all con - sum - ing fi - re, you're the rea - son why we're liv-ing

Copyright © 2010 Bethel Music Publishing /Thankyou Music Adm. by worshiptogether.com Songs excl. UK & Europe, adm. by Kingswaysongs,
a division of David C Cook tym@kingsway.co.uk /Christajoy Music (BMI)/Christa Black are admin by Bethel Music Publishing)
all rights reserved Used by Permission

high - er— and high - er,— Lord.— Be lift - ed— high, be

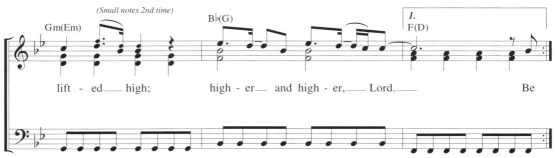

*(Small notes 2nd time)*

lift - ed— high; high - er— and high - er,— Lord.— Be

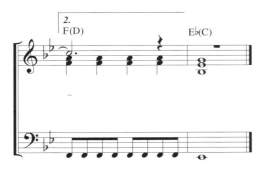

Lift up your heads,
        O you gates;
**be lifted up,**
        you ancient doors,
that the King of glory may come in

*Psalm 24:7*

29

# 8

# Be merciful

Key=F

Original Words: Josiah Conder (1789-1855)
Words adapted and original Music: Phil Moore

Capo 3 (D)

Flowing — *Verse*

1. Be mer - ci - ful, O God of grace, show us the
vine oh, let it spread, till all the
Lord, your sav - ing plan to all the
joy your prais - es sing, earth's right - eous
bar - ren world as - sume new beau - ty

brigh - tness of your face, that your re - deem - ed church may
dark - ness shall have fled. This fal - len world's dark fad - ing
fa - mi - lies of man; let dis - tant na - tions hear your
Judge and sov - 'reign King. Di - rec - ted by your ho - ly
and the des - ert bloom. Our God shall rich - ly bless us

*Last time to Coda*

**1.,3.**

shine in this dark world with light di - vine.
ray be lost in the bright light of
word let ev - 'ry peo - ple praise the Lord.
word, let all the na - tions praise the
then, and all men fear his name, a -

*D.C. (v.2,4)* **2.,4.** *Chorus*

2. That life di - day.
4. Let them with Lord.
Oh, church a - rise and pro - claim the

Copyright © 2011 Phil Moore Cornerstone Worship
www.cornerstoneworship.co.uk Used by Permission

Chords above the staves: Gm7(Em), B♭2(G), Dm7(Bm7), Csus4(A), C(A), Gm7(Em), B♭(G)

glo-ry of his name; let the na — tions sing of Christ the ri - sen

F(D), F/B♭(D), Dm7(Bm7), B♭2(G), *D.C. (vv.3,5.) al Coda*

King.

3. Re - veal, O⸺
5. Then shall this⸺

⊕ *Coda* F(D)

- men.

# God's created Church

God, you created your church,
**_this is your brilliant idea!_**

God, you created your church,
**_shine through us!_**

God, you created your church,
**_give us power!_**

God, you created your church,
**_help us love!_**

God, you created your church,
**_make us one!_**

God, you created your church,
**_take us on!_**

© Nick Harding

# 9

# Before the world
## (With us)

Key=D
Reuben Morgan
& Dylan Thomas

Rock

**Verse**

1. Be - fore the world,_____ you knew_____ the plans_____ for_____ me;
_____ I know_____ you'll an - swer_____ me,

be - fore my heart_____ be - lieved,_____ you came_____ to my_____ res - cue.
you'll make a way_____ bey - ond_____ what I_____ could i - ma - gine.

*(v.2)*

Now I'm found_____ in love,_____ there's no-where else_____ to run;
What could se - pa - rate_____ from the love_____ you gave;

_____ you keep my_____ life_____ with - in_____ your migh - ty_____ hand,
_____ I put my_____ hope_____ in ev - 'ry - thing_____ that you_____ are,_____

Copyright © 2010 Hillsong Publishing
www.hillsongpublishing.com Used by Permission

An exploration of the challenges of 'being church' in the 21st Century

"A vision of what the church can be"
– ROB PARSONS

CHURCH ACTUALLY
REDISCOVERING THE BRILLIANCE OF GOD'S PLAN

GERARD KELLY

Following the theme of Spring Harvest 2012, Gerard Kelly rediscovers the brilliance of God's plan for the church.

Available from EssentialChristian.com or your local Christian bookstore

essential christian

# 10 Before the world was made
## (Glory to God forever)

Key=B

Steve Fee
& Vicky Beeching

Capo 4(G)

Moderately

**Verse**

1. Be - fore the world was— made, be - fore you spoke it to be,
2. Cre - a - tor God, you— gave me breath so I could— praise

You were the King of— kings, yeah, you were, yeah, you were.
Your great and match - less— name all my days, all my days.

And now you're reign - ing— still, en - throned a - bove all— things;
So let my whole life— be a blaz - ing of - fer - ing,

an - gels and saints cry— out, we join them as we sing.—
a life that shouts and— sings the great - ness of our King.

Copyright © 2009 Thankyou Music/Worship Together Music/Sixsteps BMI Designee/Adm. by worshiptogether.com Songs, excl. UK & Europe
adm. by Kingswaysongs, a division of David C Cook tym@kingsway.co.uk Used by Permission

# 11

# Bless the Lord, O my soul
## (10,000 reasons)

Key=G

Matt Redman
& Jonas Myrin

With strength

Copyright © 2011 Thankyou Music/Said And Done Music/Adm. by worshiptogether.com Songs excl. UK & Europe,
adm. by Kingswaysongs, a division of David C Cook tym@kingsway.co.uk & Jonas Myrin/SHOUT! Publishing/
adm. by Hillsong Publishing publishing@hillsong.com Used by Permission

# Break our hearts

Key=F

Capo 3(D)

Vicky Beeching

Moderately *Chorus*

Break our hearts with the things that break yours, wake us up to see through your eyes. Break our hearts with the things that break yours, and send us out to shine in the dark-ness.

*Last time to Coda*

*3rd time D.C.*
*Verse*

1. It's
2. It's

Copyright © 2009 Thankyou Music/Adm. by worshiptogether.com Songs excl. UK & Europe, adm. by Kingswaysongs/Integrity Worship Music/
Adm. by EMICMGPublishing.com, excl. UK admin. by Kingswaysongs, a division of David C Cook tym@kingsway.co.uk Used by Permission

time for us to live the songs we sing, and
time to move out-side our com-fort zones, to

turn our good in-ten-tions in-to ac-tions; to
see be-yond our church-es and our homes; to

bring the kind of wor-ship you de-sire, and
change the way we think and how we spend, un-

move be-yond our self-ab-sorbed dis-trac-tions. The moun-tains are shak-ing,
til we look like Je - sus a-gain.

could this be a great a-wak-en - ing?

*This one sounds great on the acoustic CD of "Fresh: New Songs for the Church"*

41

We will shine,—— we will shine,—— we will shine,——

we will shine.——

# *Singing Scripture*

## *by Graham Kendrick*

Can we engage in sung worship together without knowing the songs, without a song list or lyrics on a screen, using 100% God-inspired words, whilst being responsive to the Holy Spirit and creatively and musically adventurous all at the same time? I say an enthusiastic 'yes'! For many years now I have enjoyed worship like this, simply by singing Scriptures straight off the page using the ancient method of 'lining out', ie. singing a line and inviting the people to sing it back. I call it Psalm Surfing, but you can call it what you like; 'Singing Scripture' works just fine.

### *What's the point of it?*
Singing is a very physical activity and engages mind, spirit and emotions simultaneously. It is said that 'one who sings prays twice', and singing God's Word can help us engage with the truth and spirit of it more deeply.

The book of Psalms begins with a promise that the person who meditates in the law of the Lord is like 'a tree planted by streams of water, which yields its fruit in season and whose leaf does not wither. Whatever he does prospers.' That is quite a promise, but in our frantic, media-intensive age it can be difficult to find space and time to 'soak our roots' in the Scriptures - if we do, many of us then find it almost impossible to quieten our information-saturated minds. Singing Scripture phrases has a similar effect as Bible meditation but with the added dynamics that music and other creative media bring.

### *What is special about it?*
Singing Scripture is open ended and takes shape as it happens, a dynamic interaction between participants and God which is infinitely variable; like a surfer trying to catch and ride waves, each with its own unique form and energy. A worship song list can be more like a train track; a pre-determined journey with points every four or five minutes where we switch to another song. Worship songs with great musical arrangements are wonderful, but what might happen if more of us became worship 'surfers' too!

## Singing Scripture (continued)

It also means that we can potentially go to any suitable Scripture, and instantly have everyone singing it!

I have found that the openness of this method makes it an ideal context where those with skills in various art forms can respond creatively, with painting, drawing, dance and movement, writing poetry and prose (or simply 'journaling' your thoughts), and of course musicians and singers can improvise.

As Scripture phrases lodge in our memories they reshape our view of God and our circumstances, enabling us to make the connection between our human condition and God's priorities, purposes and provisions for us. Whereas our own worship and prayer vocabulary becomes exhausted or narrow or the issue looms so large that faith falters, in singing Scripture God's perspective and agenda become ours.

### In what settings can it be used?
It is good for personal devotion (which is a good place to start if you are a beginner!), small group worship, music team and choir rehearsals, prayer meetings, dedicated sessions where there is no other agenda but 'waiting on God' (at the time of writing we do an hour and a half session once a month on a Sunday evening at my home church).

### What skills are required?
It is a team exercise and within that team there needs to be singers and musicians with improvisational skills and Spiritual sensitivity. Songwriters will already be familiar with putting words to music. For public settings the ability to lead wisely and make people feel secure, to keep it authentic and enjoyable is a great advantage.

### What do I do to get started?
* Practice in private / in your core music team
* Wait on God for direction
* Manage peoples' expectations - a briefing flyer and short demonstration on arrival can be helpful if it is new
* Assess the people and situation present and pitch it at an appropriate level

* Choose a key, set a tempo, 'imagine' the first line, sing it, or read until the words 'sing'
* Identify a 'refrain' that all could sing
* Give clear verbal cues ie. 'listen' 'repeat' 'sing after me'
* Make space for reflection / silence / instrumental / poetic / artistic / dance 'moments' etc
* Stop occasionally and invite verbal feedback
* Reinforce any emerging theme
* Evaluate, correct anything unhelpful, keep a recorder running or have notes taken for review afterwards

### Musical leadership options:
It can be led with unaccompanied voice / voice and percussion / self-accompanied voice / one sings, another plays accompaniment / 'follow my fingers' (sight-lines essential) / follow a repeating chord cycle. I like to lead it 'in the round' on floor level with the musicians as the innermost circle, facing inwards and across to each other for optimum visual communication, which also engenders a sense of community in the room.

### Which Scriptures?
Anything that can be said can be sung, but obviously the Psalms, Poetry and Wisdom Books, and the prophetic books are most lyrical and therefore most sing-able. Scripture on screen is ok, but a 'Bible-in-hand' approach enables people to read backwards and forwards and reflect at their own pace (same translation if possible).

### Oops!
Avoid boring repetition (if you sing yourself into a 'dead end' just stop and start again), and gratuitous jamming (musicians having their own meeting, oblivious that everyone else has disengaged). Keep Scripture within its context, and read ahead as you go so you can decide whether you want to go there or not.

*Have a go and don't be scared to make mistakes – it's the best way to learn!*

*Graham Kendrick*
*www.grahamkendrick.co.uk*

# 13 Christ be in my waking

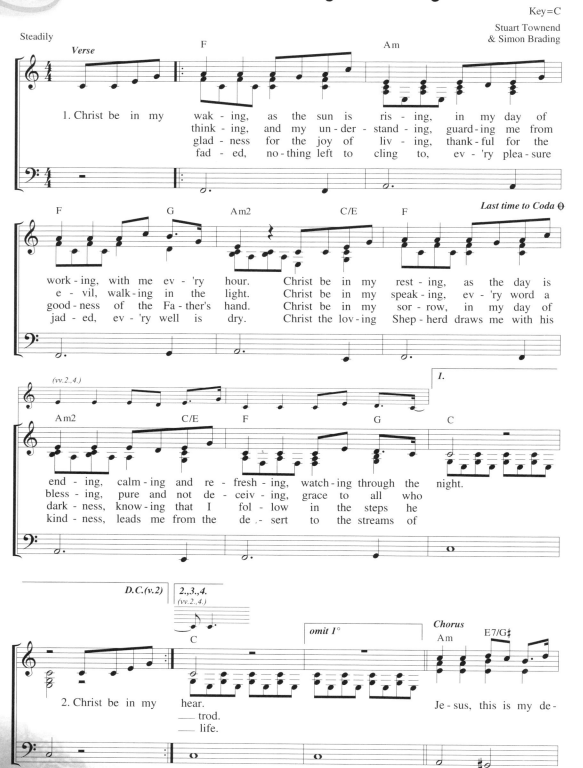

Copyright © 2011 Thankyou Music/Adm. by worshiptogether.com Songs excl. UK & Europe, adm. by Kingswaysongs,
a division of David C Cook tym@kingsway.co.uk Used by Permission

# 14 Come and join the singing
## (Sing it out)

Key=E
Dave Bilbrough

Capo 2(D)

With celebration

Copyright © 2011 Dave Bilbrough Songs
Used by Permission

raise an an - them to our God.

Last time to Coda ⊕    1.,3.,5.,6.,7.        2.        D.C. (v.2)

Mid section

Be - gin to pro - phe - sy, wo - oh - woh.

The low-est val-ley shall be lift-ed high, wo-oh-woh. Ev-'ry moun-tain and

hill made low in the name of the Lord. E-ne-mies are

# Power potential

Lord, help us to fulfil our God-given potential to play our part within your church.

Lord, encourage us to find our identity not in what we do but in who you are.

Lord, enable us to build your kingdom now that we might be ready for when you return as King.

*Amen.*

© 2011 Marie Birkinshaw

AVAILABLE JULY 2012
PRE-ORDER NOW

Spring Harvest

**LIVE WORSHIP ACTUALLY**

LIVE PRAISE AND WORSHIP FROM THE SPRING HARVEST BIG TOP
VICKY BEECHING | MARK BESWICK | PETE JAMES | GERALDINE LATTY

## WITH WORSHIP LEADERS:-

VICKY BEECHING

MARK BESWICK

PETE JAMES

GERALDINE LATTY

## LIVE WORSHIP FROM
## SPRING HARVEST 2012

Awe-inspiring live worship
from Spring Harvest's Big Top

Available from EssentialChristian.com
or your local Christian bookstore

essential christian

# 15 Come breathe on us now
## (Come breathe)

Key=D

Dave Bilbrough

Quite freely

1. Come breathe on us now, God of all grace, God of all
2. Speak straight to our hearts, re-mind us a-gain your na-ture is

pow'r. Your Spi-rit is here and hum-bly we bow to ho-nour
love. Free-ly you gave, en-dur-ing that cross that we might

you.
live. You de-serve the high - est praise.

You de-serve the high - est praise.

Copyright © 2011 Dave Bilbrough Songs
Used by Permission

*2nd time D.C (v.1) al Coda*       *Verse*

3. Be our guid-ing light, the One we a-

dore, our pearl of great price. Cre-a-tor of all, we o-pen our

lives to know your truth.

**Coda**

you.

# Come on, my soul

Key=E

Rend Collective Experiment

Capo 4(C)

Gently rhythmic

Copyright © 2008 Thankyou Music/Adm. by worshiptogether.com Songs excl. UK & Europe, adm. by kingswaysongs.com, a division of David C Cook tym@kingsway.co.uk Used by Permission.

Come on, come on, come on, come on, it's

time to — look up. _____ Come _____ Come

sing my — soul.

I can do *everything* through **him** who who gives me **strength**

*Philippians 4:13*

# 17 Form us

Key=F

Casey Corum
& Anabeth Morgan

Capo 3(D)
Steadily, with feeling

1. Form us, make us, mould us, shape us,
2. Move us, lead us, send us, re-lease us

to be like you, moved to ac-tion, full of mer-cy
to the bro-ken, to the hun-gry, to the out-cast,

*1.* and com-pas-sion. *2.* and com-pas-sion.
to the wea-ry. to the wea-ry. Our hearts say

yes, Lord, come take con-trol. In us, in us,

come have your way, O Lord, in us, in us, your way. In

Copyright © 2010 Mercy/Vineyard Publishing/Admin by Song Solutions CopyCare
www.songsolutions.org Used by Permission

mer - cy tri - umphs o - ver judge - ment,_____ mer - cy tri - umphs o - ver judge-

B♭sus2(G)                    F/A(D/F♯)            Gm7(Em)

**Mid section II**

ment._____ We say yes,_____ Lord,_____ we say yes,_____ Lord,

F(D)                     B♭sus2(G)          F/A(D/F♯)          Gm7(Em)

F(D)                                   B♭sus2(G)

_____ We say yes,_____ Lord,

R.H.

**1.**
F/A(D/F♯)          Gm7(Em)           Dm7(Bm7)                **2.**
                                                                   F/A(D/F♯)

_____ we say yes,_____ we say yes._____ We say yes,- _____ we say yes.-

# God is able

Key=B

Very rhythmic

Ben Fielding & Reuben Morgan
Arrangement by: Michael Guy Chislett

1. God is a - ble,_____ he will ne - ver fail,_____
with__ us,_____ God is on our side,_____

he is Al-migh - ty God;____ great - er than all we see,____ great - er than
he will make__ a__ way.____ Far__ a-bove all we__ know, far__ a-bove

all we__ ask,____ he has done__ great__ things.____ Lift-ed up,__
all we__ hope,____ he has done__ great__ things.____

____ he de-feat - ed the grave;____ raised to life,____ our God is a-

Copyright © 2010 Hillsong Publishing www.hillsongpublishing.com
Used by Permission

**SPRING HARVEST**
**s**ng search

If you need help to find a song on a particular
theme or Scripture passage, or just want to know
which of the Spring Harvest songbooks or albums
features the song you're after - use our song search.

» search online at *www.springharvest.org/songsearch*

# 19 God so loved, loved this world
## (Salvation day)

Capo 3(D)

Key=F
Vicky Beeching &
Jonny & Sarah MacIntosh

Positively

1. God so loved, loved this world, that he gave his Son;
2. I so love, love your world, that I'll give my life

— who-e-ver would put their trust, put their trust in him, would live for-e-
— so they would, yes they would see your sa-cri-fice, and live for-e-

-ver, live for-e-ver. God your love, so di-
-ver, live for-e-ver. The same love we've re-

vine, it has found me here; lift-ed me from the
ceived we will give a-way; we will shine in the

grave, wiped a-way my tears: I'm yours for-e-ver,
dark 'til it's bright as day, 'cause we're so grate-ful,

Copyright © 2009/11 Thankyou Music/Adm. by worshiptogether.com Songs excl. UK & Europe, adm. by Kingswaysongs/Integrity Worship Music/
Adm. by EMICMGPublishing.com, excl. UK admin. by Kingswaysongs, a division of David C Cook tym@kingsway.co.uk Used by Permission

# Prayer for equipping

Where humility is in short supply,
God grant us servant hearts,
**As we seek to be followers of Christ.**

Where many live in the darkness of injustice,
God make us beacons of hope,
**As we seek to bring the light of Christ.**

Where we encounter barriers and stagnation,
God make us channels of positive change,
**As we seek to share your transforming love.**

Where there is division and dissention,
God make us communities of blessing,
**As we seek to restore your harmony and peace.**

*© 2011 Marie Birkinshaw*

# 20 God, you are my God

Key=C

Pete James

Worshipfully ♩ = 78

**Verse**

1. God, you are my God, ear-nest-ly I seek you.
2. God, you are my God, ear-nest-ly I seek you.

God, you are my God, ear-nest-ly I seek you;
God, you are my God, ear-nest-ly I seek you;

and my soul longs for you,
and my soul be-longs to you,

**2nd time to Coda**

and my soul longs for you,
and my soul be-longs to

longs for you.

Copyright © 2011 Song Solutions Daybreak
www.songsolutions.org Used by Permission

# 21

# Great is your love
## (Alive in us)

Key=G

Reuben Morgan
& Jason Ingram

Steadily

**Verse**

1. Great is your love,___ let the whole earth___ sing, let the whole earth___ sing.
2. You out-shine the sun,___ you are glo-ri-ous, you are glo-ri-ous.

You reached for us___ from on hea-ven's___ throne
Lord o-ver all,___ you have made us___ new,

when we had no___ hope. You are the___ way there is no
we owe it all to___ you. In ev'-ry-thing be ex-

o-ther; you are the___ way there is no o-ther.___ You
al-ted; in ev'-ry-thing be ex-al-ted.

**Chorus**

rose from death to vic-to-ry, you reign in life, O

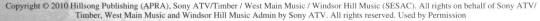
Copyright © 2010 Hillsong Publishing (APRA), Sony ATV/Timber / West Main Music / Windsor Hill Music (SESAC). All rights on behalf of Sony ATV/ Timber, West Main Music and Windsor Hill Music Admin by Sony ATV. All rights reserved. Used by Permission

Majesty. Your name be high and lift-ed up; Jesus, Je-sus a-live in us.
in us. You in us.
The e-ne-my is un-der your feet, we are free, we are free.

*Last time to Coda* ⊕

*1.*

*D.C. (v.2)*

*3.*

*D.S. al Coda*

*2.*

*Mid section*

69

Death has been de-feat-ed by love, you o-ver-come, you o-ver-come.

**1.** The

**2.** You

**Coda**

in us. Je-sus, Je-sus a-live in us.

**Jesus** answered " **I am the way** the **truth** and the **life.**

No-one comes to the **Father** except through me "

*John 14:6*

# 22

# Hallelujah, rejoice
## (Resting in love)

Joyfully

Key=C

Karla Drader

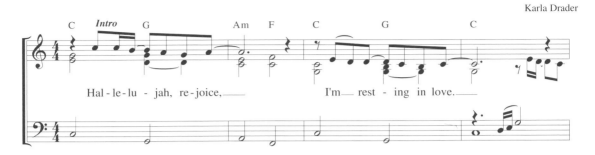

Hal - le - lu - jah, re - joice,____ I'm____ rest - ing in love.____

Hal - le - lu - jah, a - men,____ I'm____ rest - ing in love.____

1. Take my heart, take my will,____ draw me clos - er un - til
2. I won't be - lieve____ the lies,____ I'm not a - lone____ or de - spised;

____ I'm rest - ing in love.____ Help me seek____ your face,
____ I'm rest - ing in love.____ I reach my hands up to you,

Copyright © 2007 Karla Drader www.karladrader.com
Used by Permission

# 23

## Here I am
### (I give myself away)

Capo 3(G)

Key=B♭

Gospel feel ♩ = 62

William Matt Dowell

1. Here I am, here I stand, Lord, my life is in your
   heart, take my life as a liv - ing sa - cri -

hands; Lord, I'm long - ing to see your de -
fice; all my dreams, all my plans, Lord, I

si - res re - vealed in me. I give my-self a-way,
place them in your hands.

I give my-self a-way, so you can use me. I give my-self a-way,

Copyright © 2008 Delivery Room Publishing (Admin by Midi Services Ltd)
Used by Permission

I give my-self a-way,___ so you can use___me. Take my___

use___me. I give my-self a-way, use___me. My life is not___my own,___ to

you I be-long; I give my-self,___ I give my-self___ to you.___ My

# 24

# Higher than the mountains that I face
## *(One thing remains)*

Key=B

Capo 4(G)

Brian Johnson, Jeremy Riddle
& Christa Black

Steadily

1. High - er than the moun - tains that I _____ face,
   on and on and on and on _____ it goes, it

stron - ger than the po - wer of the _____ grave,
o - ver - whelms and sa - tis - fies _____ my soul. And I

con - stant in the tri - al and the change, this one thing re -
ne - ver, e - ver have to be a - fraid; this one _____ thing re -

Copyright © 2010 Bethel Music / Mercy/Vineyard Publishing/Admin by Song Solutions CopyCare
www.songsolutions.org Used by Permission

Don't know this one?
Don't worry! — you can hear it on
"Fresh: New songs for the Church"

hear samples and
buy online

# 25 History split by sacrifice
## (Acquitted)

Key=B

Capo 4(G)

Jeremy Riddle
& Jeremy Edwardson

Steadily, with a strong beat

1. Hi - sto - ry split by sa - cri - fice,
2. True love was shown, true love de - fined,

God's per - fect Son gave up his life,
as he was scorned and cru - ci - fied;

to ran - som back the lost and damned,
he tore the veil, bridged the di - vide,

pay - ing the price jus - tice de - mands. As he was bro - ken,
tak - ing us from dark - ness to light.

hea - ven was o - pened, our judge - ment lift - ed, our sins ac - quit - ted;

Copyright © 2011 Mercy/Vineyard Publishin/Admin by Song Solutions CopyCare www.songsolutions.org/ Jeremy Edwardson Music
(Admin by VineyardMusic.com & Jeremy Edwardson Music. Used by Permission

# Fresh: New Songs for the Church

**22 new songs to inspire the church in worship**

- **2 CDs featuring full band and acoustic arrangements**
- **Music scores for all the songs are available in this songbook**

*Scan here to listen to track samples or buy online* →

**Available from EssentialChristian.com or your local Christian bookstore**

# 26 Holy Father rich in mercy

Key=D

Phil Moore
& Colin Webster

1. Holy Father rich in mercy, holy Saviour rich in grace; great in glory everlasting, how I long to see your face. Lead me to your new creation, lead me to your throne of love; giving glory to the Father, to the Spirit and the

Christ our risen Saviour, Shepherd of the weak and lost; Author of our great salvation through the power of the cross. Lead from glory into glory, safely held by arms of love; so to dwell with you forever, bringing praises to our

Spirit breath of heaven, make me holy through your word; break the chains of sin's destruction, fix my eyes upon you Lord. When I wander from your safety, when I wander from your truth, draw me back to my Redeemer, through the Holy fire of

Copyright © 2011 Phil Moore & Colin Webster Cornerstone Worship
www.cornerstoneworship.co.uk Used by Permission

# Hope fills my soul
## (Glorious)

Key=E

Bryan & Katie Torwalt

Capo 2(D)

With a strong beat

Copyright © 2011 Bryan & Katie Torwalt All right admin by Jesus Culture Music
Used by Permission

**Mid section**

A(G)          C♯m(Bm)         *1.-3.* E(D)

sound of— our praise, the hea-vens— will shake— and the earth will move.

B(A)          *4.* E(D)         B(A)         *D.S.*

And at the earth will move.———— You are—

For **great** *is the* **Lord** and most worthy of **praise;** **he** is to be feared above **all** gods

*1 Chronicles 16:25*

# 28

# Hope is here
## (Jesus saves)

Key=C

Tim Hughes
& Nick Herbert

Rock ♩ = 130

**Verse**

1. Hope is here,_____ shout the news____ to ev-'ry-one,_____ it's a new
_____ ev-'ry debt____ has been__ re-paid,_____ bro-ken hearts__

Am | F | C

__ day, peace__ has come:_____ Je - sus__ saves.____ Mer-cy tri-
__ can be re-made:_____ Je - sus__ saves.____ Sing a-bove__

- umphs at__ the cross,____ love has come____ to res - cue us:____
__ the storms__ of life,____ sing it through____ the dark - est night:__

Am | F | C

__ Je - sus__ saves.____
__ Je - sus__ saves.____

Copyright © 2008 Thankyou Music/Adm. by worshiptogether.com Songs excl. UK & Europe,
adm. by Kingswaysongs, a division of David C Cook tym@kingsway.co.uk Used by Permission

you heal,— re-store,— re-veal— your Fa - ther's heart— to us.— You rose—

to raise— us from— the grave; your Spi - rit lives— in— us.— Sing it out,—

*Coda*

You save,———— you save,

you save!————

# Hosanna in the highest
## (Hosanna/Be lifted up)

# 29

Key=A

Copyright © 2010 Integrity's Praise! Music/ Sound of The New Breed/ Adm. by EMICMGPublishing.com, excl. UK admin. by Kingswaysongs,
a division of David C Cook tym@kingsway.co.uk & True Worshippers Productions/KI Publishing
(Adm. by Song Solutions CopyCare www.songsolutions.org) Used by Permission

# 30
# How great is your love
## (All glory)

Key=C

Nikki Fletcher, Tim Hughes
& Martin Smith

Thoughtfully ♩ = 78

1. How great is your love, that ne-ver gives up on me.
2. So great is your love, it keeps all your pro - mi-ses.

Stron-ger than shame, it car-ries me back to you.
Un-shak - a - ble, e-ter-ni-ty rests in your

Je-sus, my re-deem - er, you have made a way.
hands. Je-sus, I sur-ren - der, lead me in your ways.

*v.2 only*

All glo - ry to God who is a - ble,

Copyright © 2010 Thankyou Music/Adm. by worshiptogether.com Songs excl. UK & Europe,
adm. by Kingswaysongs & Curious? Music/Adm. by Kingswaysongs tym@kingsway.co.uk Used by Permission

# 31 How strong did darkness appear?
## (Glory to the Lamb)

Key=B

Capo 4(G)

Jeremy Riddle
& Christa Black

Moderate rock

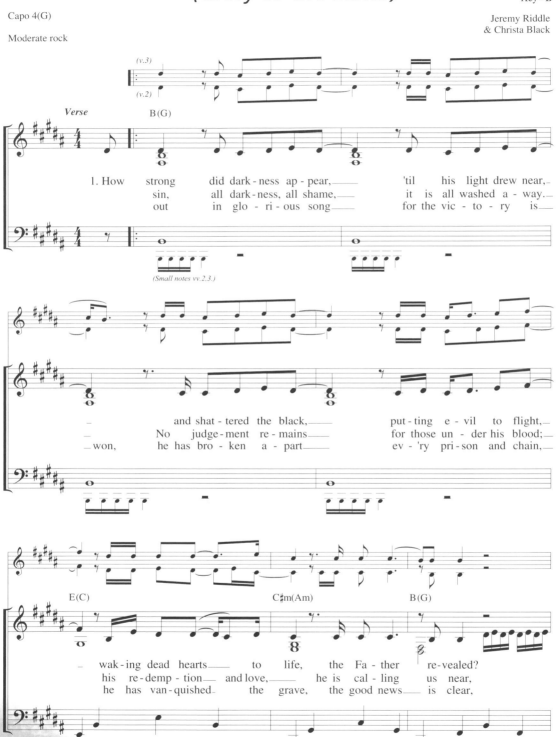

Verse

B(G)

1. How strong did dark-ness ap-pear,_____ 'til his light drew near,_____
sin, all dark-ness, all shame,_____ it is all washed a-way._
out in glo-ri-ous song_____ for the vic-to-ry is_

(Small notes vv.2.3.)

_____ and shat-tered the black,_____ put-ting e-vil to flight,_
_ No judge-ment re-mains_____ for those un-der his blood;
_won, he has bro-ken a-part_____ ev-'ry pri-son and chain,_

E(C)                    C#m(Am)                B(G)

_ wak-ing dead hearts_____ to life, the Fa-ther re-vealed?
his re-demp-tion_____ and love,_____ he is cal-ling us near,
he has van-quished_ the grave, the good news_____ is clear,

Copyright © 2011 Mercy/Vineyard Publishing/Admin by Song Solutions CopyCare
www.songsolutions.org & Christa Joy Music Publishing Used by Permission

sal - va - tion__ is here.__

2. All    no rea - son left__ to fear.__

Come let us wor-ship and a - dore, kneel-ing lo-wer now be-

fore  him,  giv - ing   glo - ry  to  the  Lamb.__

3. Break

Come and wor-ship Christ the Sa-viour, come with joy—and of-fer-ings;

come and wor-ship Christ the Sa-viour, come, a-dore—the King of kings.

# 32

# I look to the cross where my hope is found
## (At the cross)

Key=C

John & Emma Mongan
& Maxwell Curd

Flowing

*Verse*

I look to the cross____ where my hope is found,

the pur - est of ____ love ____ by grave poured ____ out.

I look to the cross____ now my pur - pose found;

shaped by your ____ love,____ in you I ____ stand, in you ____ I

____ stand.____ At the cross____ I sur - ren - der,

Copyright © 2011 Song Solutions Daybreak
www.songsolutions.org Used by Permission

# 33

# I want to scream it out
## (You are good)

Key=B

Brian Johnson
& Jeremy Riddle

Capo 4(G)
Steadily, with a strong beat

1. I want to scream it out from ev-'ry moun-tain top,
2. No-thing and no one comes a-ny-where close to you,

your good-ness knows no bounds, your good-ness ne-ver stops,
the earth and o-ceans deep on-ly re-flect this truth,

your mer-cy fol-lows me, your kind-ness fills my life,
and in my dark-est night you shine as bright as day,

your love a-maz-es me. And I'll
your love a-maz-es me.

sing be-cause you are good, and I'll dance be-cause you are good, and I'll

Copyright © 2010 Mercy/Vineyard Publishing/Admin by Song Solutions CopyCare
www.songsolutions.org (Admin by Bethel Music & VineyardMusic.com) Used by Permission

We really enjoyed recording this song for the "FRESH New Songs for the Church" CD

# 34

# I will exalt you

Key=B

Brooke Ligertwood

Steady 4

Copyright © 2009 Sony/ATV Music Publishing Australia (Aust. & NZ only),
Hillsong Publishing (Rest of world) Used by Permission

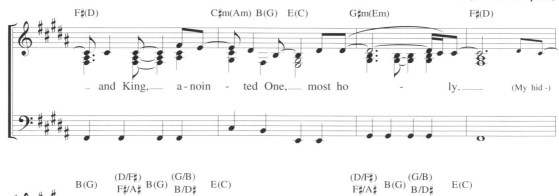

... and King,___ a-noin - ted One,___ most ho - ly.___ (My hid -)

2. Be - cause you're

# SPRING HARVEST
# **s⌕ng** search

If you need help to find a song on a particular theme or Scripture passage, or just want to know which of the Spring Harvest songbooks or albums features the song you're after - use our song search.

» search online at **www.springharvest.org/songsearch**

# 35 If God had a mobile phone
## (Open the pages)

Key=B♭

Capo 3(G)

Vicky Beeching

Joyfully ♩ = 136

**Verse**

1. If God had a mo-bile phone____ and he sent you a text,
God sent you an e - mail,____ typ-ing a - way,____

what would it say?____ Guess what? We al - rea - dy know,____ 'cause he's

writ-ten it down,____ page____ af - ter page.____ It's called the Bi - ble, an a -

maz-ing book,____ it's called the Bi - ble, just take a - no-ther look.____ As we

o - o - o - o - o - o-pen the pa - ges, Lord we love to read your sto-ry. O - o - o - o -

Copyright © 2011 Vicky Beeching
Used by Permission

# 36

# If I searched the heavens
## (Your love reaches)

Capo 4(G)

Key=B

Steadily ♩ = 72

Sam Parker, Jamie Rodwell, Graham Kendrick,
Chris Sayburn & Simon Francis

1. If I searched the hea - vens, all of cre - a -
2. And though I have tast - ed what this world of -

- tion, could a - ny - thing com - pare?
- fers, it ne - ver sa - tis - fies;

With what I've dis - co - vered, fill - ing my vi -
but now I will be what your love makes

sion, I can only stand and stare. Your
me, I'm see - ing with new eyes. Your

Copyright © 2011 Thankyou Music/Adm. by worshiptogether.com Songs excl. UK & Europe, adm. by Kingswaysongs,
a division of David C Cook tym@kingsway.co.uk & Make Way Music www.grahamkendrick.co.uk
International copyright secured. All rights reserved. Used by Permission

111

# If my heart is overwhelmed
## (Love came down)

37

Key=C

Copyright © 2009 Bethel Music (Admin by Bethel Music)/Mercy/Vineyard Publishing (Admin by Song Solutions CopyCare www.songsolutions.org)
Ian McIntosh Publishing/Jeremy Edwardson Music (Admin by Jeremy Edwardson) Used by Permission

G  *Bridge*  Dm7  C/E  G

I'll re - mind my-self  of  all that you've done,_____  and the

*(2°)*

Dm7  C/E  F

life  I___ have  be - cause  of  your Son._____
(life  I  have)

*Chorus*  C  F

Love came down and  re - scued me,  love came down and  set me free,  and

Am  G  F

I  am yours,_____  God, I'm  for - e - ver yours.

C  F

Moun - tain high  or  val - ley low,  I sing out,  re - mind my soul  that

114

# 38

# I'm bringing my sound
## (In this forever)

Key=D

Rita Springer

Flowing ♩. = 123

**Verse**

1. I'm bring-ing my sound,_____ giv-ing you all my wor - ship,
2. You, you give me life,_____ you give me all my free - dom.

I'm here to bow down,_____ tell you that you are worth it._ And_ I_
You, you ne - ver change,_____ and you have no turn-ing ei - ther._ And_ I_

_____ throw up my hands,_____ and I com - plete - ly sur-ren - der;
_____ throw up my hands,_____ and I com - plete - ly sur-ren - der;_____

(v.2)

all I have found_____ in you is so_ much bet - ter.
all that I have found_____ in you is so_ much bet - ter. And I,_

**Chorus**

Copyright © 2010 Integrity's Praise! Music/Adm. by EMICMGPublishing.com, excl. UK admin. by Kingswaysongs,
a division of David C Cook tym@kingsway.co.uk Used by Permission

117

# God's presence leads to God's promises

## by Andy Smith

Proximity makes a big difference. For instance, it's much easier to talk about your boss when they're not standing right in front of you - or think of it this way - I remember being alone in my room rehearsing a grand confession of love to a girl, only to find, being in the same room as this girl caused my eloquence to dissolve in sweat as my armpits conspired against me. Christian worship has so much 'love' rhetoric, that it's really easy to sound like we're actually in love. And so often, we get through times of worship without the heart-pounding, butt-clenching reality of being face to face with Jesus.

When everything had been finished (the lampstand, the altar, ark, the curtain - all the dressings and furnishings complete) then the cloud covered the tent of meeting and the glory of the Lord filled the tabernacle. When the cloud lifted and moved, they followed; when it rested, they stayed. A cloud by day, fire by night - the presence of God led the people of Israel to the promises of God.

When we're trying to do church in a way that is progressive, missional, about others - we're the kind of people who have a horizon, a destination. Most of the time, it's as if the horizon is constantly moving.

It's like manna - hand to mouth (crazy how we can despise familiar miracles). Easy to get disappointed. What we long for is the wide and spacious place where we can flourish - livestock, crops - multiplication. God's presence led them to that place. Religion is going through the motions, form without power, Sinai without crossing the Jordan - it won't get us there. It is the dangerous, unpredictable, vulnerable, open hearted experience of being in the presence of God that will lead us to a place of promise.

He is the Immanuel - God with us.

Proximity makes a big difference.

*Andy Smith*

**Look out for a new album by Andy Smith coming from Elevation in 2012!**

# 39

# I'm standing at the cross
## (Standing at the cross)

Key=G

Pete James

Copyright © 2011 Song Solutions Daybreak
www.songsolutions.org Used by Permission

why you love me just the way I am.___ There's no great-er

love than this, that the Son___ of God___ would lay down___ his life___ for me.___

There's no great-er life to live than the one___ you give,___ it's a mi-

-ra-cle___ to me.___

3. In bro-ken-ness___ I kneel___
4. Your bo-dy bears___ the scars___

There's no great-er ___ Mi-ra-cle___ to me.

Have you heard the acoustic version of this song on the "FRESH: New Songs for the Church" CD?

121

# 40

# In the beginning
## (Breath of God)

Key=B

Vicky Beeching

Capo 4(G)

With increasing intensity

**Verse**

1. In the be-gin-ning was dark-ness and no-thing, your
2. Bones in a val-ley were changed in-to an ar-my,

Spi-rit was mo-ving o-ver the deep.
raised by your Spi-rit's po-wer-ful touch.

You spoke a whis-per and cre-a-tion ex-ist-ed,
Here in your pre-sence, I'm need-ing your re-fresh-ing;

birthed by the migh-ty words that you speak.
Lord, please re-vive my heart with your love.

**Bridge**

Just say the

Copyright © 2008 Thankyou Music Adm. by worshiptogether.com Songs excl. UK & Europe,
adm. by Kingswaysongs, a division of David C Cook tym@kingsway.co.uk Used by Permission

word_____ and my wea - ry soul_____ will be re - newed.

**𝄋 Chorus**

Breathe on me O_____ breath of God and fill_____ me with

life a - new. Breathe on me O_____

breath of God and set this heart on fire_____ for you._____

123

# DIGITAL SONGBOOK FEATURING OVER 450 SONGS FROM THE SPRING HARVEST PRAISE 2006–2010 SONGBOOKS

**THE WORSHIP YEARS DIGITAL SONGBOOK 2006 → 2010**

FEATURING DIGITAL SHEET MUSIC AND GUITAR CHORDS FOR OVER 450 SONGS FROM THE SPRING HARVEST PRAISE 2006–2010 SONGBOOKS

Powered by *PowerMusic lite*
MUSIC MANAGEMENT SOFTWARE

- Transpose chord sheets instantly
- Add capo chords in any key; show fret number
- Mac users can access the chords and scores as PDFs

**Available from EssentialChristian.com or your local Christian bookstore**

essential christian

# 41

## Into a world so bruised by sin
### (I will say my God is glorious)

Key=B♭

Words: Colin Webster
Music: Colin Webster & Phil Moore

Steadily

Capo 3(G)

1. In-to a world so bruised by sin came the Sa - viour, Christ the
walk to - wards the cross, a bat - tle won in ev - 'ry

Lord, speak-ing out God's word of hope to heal the bro-ken and the
stride; as cru-el nails were dri-ven home, the wrath of God up-on him

lost. The blind now see, the deaf now hear, the dead are
lay. Bu-ried with him, my guilt and shame, no con-dem-

Copyright © 2011 Phil Moore & Colin Webster Cornerstone Worship
www.cornerstoneworship.co.uk Used by Permission

raised at his com - mand; but great - er still, Christ took my sin, And I will
na - tion now I dread, for e - ven death has lost its sting, when from the

**Chorus**

glo - ry in the cross.
grave Christ rose a - gain.
I will say my God is glo - ri - ous, the

Christ who died for me; I will say my God is glo - ri - ous: the

Lamb of Cal - va - ry. He bore my guilt, my con - dem - na - tion, hid - den in

*Last time to Coda*

Christ, my sin is gone, I will say my God is glo - ri - ous: the Lamb up - on the

You see, at just the **right time**, when **we** were still *powerless*, **Christ** died for the *ungodly*

*Romans 5:6*

# 42

# Into your arms
## (Closer/Wrap me in your arms)

Key=D♭

Capo 1(C)

William McDowell

Steady gospel feel ♩ = 65

Lyrics:

Verse:
In-to your arms, I'm draw-ing near a-gain,
to dwell with you, it's my on-ly heart's de-sire,
it's my on-ly heart's de-sire.

All I can do, is fall on my knees and cry;
cleanse me with fire, and pu-ri-fy my heart.

Chorus:
Draw me close, clos-er than be-fore,

Copyright © William McDowell info@williammcdowellmusic.com
Used by Permission

closer than I've ever been. Draw me

close, closer than before, closer than I've e-

- ver been. - ver been.

Draw me - ver been. Wrap me in your arms,

wrap me in your arms, wrap me in your arms, O God.

# It is by grace that we are saved

## (Adore him)

# 43

Steadily, with ambiance

Key=D
Samuel Lane

1. It is by grace that we are saved,
2. So we've been raised with Je - sus Christ,

through faith and not by works;
let's set our hearts on things a - bove,

for it is through Je -
that we may be filled

- sus that we have life,
with the full - ness of God,

Copyright © 2010 Vineyard Songs (UK/Eire)/Admin by Song Solutions CopyCare
www.songsolutions.org Used by Permission

We had a great time recording this song on the "FRESH: New Songs for the Church" CD

# 44

# Jesus, at the center of it all

Key=A

Israel Houghton, Adam Ranney
& Micah Massey

Copyright © Integrity's Praise! Music/Sound Of The New Breed/Adm. by EMICMGPublishing.com, excl. UK admin. by Kingswaysongs,
a division of David C Cook tym@kingsway.co.uk & Micah Massey Designee/Adam Raney Designee Used by Permission

137

all a - bout you. From my   all a - bout you,

all a - bout you,

There's a really great acoustic version of this song on the "FRESH: New Songs for the Church" CD

"I am the Alpha and the Omega, the First and the Last, the Beginning and the End"

Revelation 22:13

# BUMPER DIGI-SONGBOOK

Includes *over 160 printable music scores* with *full thematic and Scripture indexes*

Featuring the music scores from all the **Kids Praise Party** and **Pre-School Praise** albums so far!

## masses of great resources for kids

### Pre-School Praise

### KIDS PRAISE PARTY

**A selection box of crazy-cool treats for little ones.** Spring Harvest Pre-School Praise Box Sets will add a splash of colour to their journey in faith!

**These box sets zoom into top gear with a combo of well known worship songs from the fast to the fantastic.** An amazing collection of thirst quenching tunes filled with the great news of Jesus!

**Available from EssentialChristian.com or your local Christian bookstore**

# 45

# Let me wait in the majesty
## (Wait)

Key=B♭

Michael Sandeman

Capo 3(G)

Tenderly

Verse

Let me wait in the ma - je - sty, find me
Let me kneel in the ra - di - ance, filled with

there; let me gaze on your glo - ry: heart bowed,
awe; let me take in the bril - li - ance, lost in

hands raised._____
won - der._____

*(Fine)* Chorus

Breath - ing in____ your love for
me,____ all a - round____ I see your
truth and beau - ty; drink - ing in____ your pu - ri -

Copyright © 2011 Phat Music/Admin by Song Solutions Copycare
www.songsolutions.org Used by Permission

We're really pleased with the version of this song we recorded for "FRESH: New Songs for the Church"... We hope you like it too!

# 46

# Let our praise be
## (Awaken me)

Key=B♭

Chris Quilala

Copyright © 2011 Jesus Culture Music
All rights reserved Admin by Jesus Culture Music Used by Permission

143

come and— fill— this— place.——

*Mid section*

Come,——————— like— you pro - mised;

come,——————— fall— up - on— us.

**elevation kids**

because kids deserve the best
www.elevationmusic.com/elevationkids

**Spring Harvest**

# the big start

A collection of favourite worship songs from the Big Start

Spring Harvest introduces the Big Start CD, a brand new resource for all-age worship, starting your day with life and colour.

Brand new CD

**DISCOVER MORE FROM ELEVATION KIDS HERE**

Available from EssentialChristian.com
or your local Christian bookstore

**essential christian**

# 47

# Let our praise be your welcome
## (Here for you)

Key=C

Matt Maher, Matt Redman,
Tim Wanstall & Jesse Reeves

With anticipation ♩ = 85

*(v.2, sung 8va)*

**Verse** C

1. { Let our praise be your wel-come, let our songs be a
   breath come from hea-ven, fill our hearts with your
2. { shout be your an-them, your re-nown fill the
   word move in po-wer, let what's dead come to

Fmaj7                    C

sign.
life. { We are here for___ you, we are here for___ you.
skies.
life.

**1.,3.**          **2.,4.**          **Chorus** 𝄋 F

Let your                    To you, our hearts are o-pen,
Let your

G                    C/E                    F

no-thing here is hid-den. you are our one de-sire.

Copyright © 2011 Thankyou Music/Said And Done Music/Valley of Songs/ worshiptogether.comSongs/sixstepsMusic/
Adm. by worshiptogether.com Songs excl. UK & Europe, adm. by Kingswaysongs, a division of David C Cook
tym@kingsway.co.uk/Chrysalis Music Ltd Used by Permission

# 48

# Let the people say

Key=A

South African feel ♩ = 120

Noel Robinson & Israel Houghton

*Chorus*

(Leader) Let the peo - ple say:— (Response) for the— Lord is— good.

(Leader) Let the na - tion's cry:— (Response) for the— Lord is— good.

(Leader) Let the chil - dren sing:— (Response) for the— Lord is— good,

(All) and his mer - cy— en - du - reth— for e - ver— and e - ver.—

Copyright © 2009 Nu Image Music (Admin by Amos3music info@ amos3music.com)/Integrity's Praise! Music/ Sound of The New Breed/
Adm. by EMICMGPublishing.com, excl. UK admin. by Kingswaysongs, a division of David C Cook tym@kingsway.co.uk Used by Permission

# Give thanks for his presence

We will shine with the light of the Lord our God,
**and give thanks for his presence.**

We will work with the power that God offers,
**and give thanks for his presence.**

We will serve others with the love that God shares,
**and give thanks for his presence.**

We will unite and grow with the grace that God pours out,
**and give thanks for his presence.**

*© Nick Harding*

# 49

# Like a shelter
## (Never changing)

Micah Nichols, James Galloway
& Martin Chalk

Key=A♭

Capo 1(G)

Driving

Copyright © 2011 Seacoast Music
Used by Permission

153

# 50

# Lord, come build your glorious Church
## (The mighty Gospel)

Key=D

Steve James

Moderately

1. Lord, come build your glo-rious Church, by your migh-ty gos-pel;
2. Lord, come build your glo-rious Church, re-fuge for the bro-ken;
3. Lord, come build your glo-rious Church, peo-ple of the pro-mise;

tel-ling of the Lord of all Christ the cru-ci-fied.
shep-herd to the way-ward heart, heal-ing soul and will.
wait-ing for that fi-nal day, earth to heav'n re-stored.

He the Lamb who bears our sin, his the pow'r of life
Mer-cy brought to re-bel lives, truth to break the de-
Where all hurts can be un-done, pain and sor-row shall

with-in, his the church where prais-es ring,
-vil's lies, peace for ev-'ry storm of life,
be gone, and on-ly Je-sus is our song,

Copyright © 2011 Steve James/ Administered by The Jubilate Group
Kitley House, St Katherines Road, Torquay, Devon TQ1 4DE Used by Permission

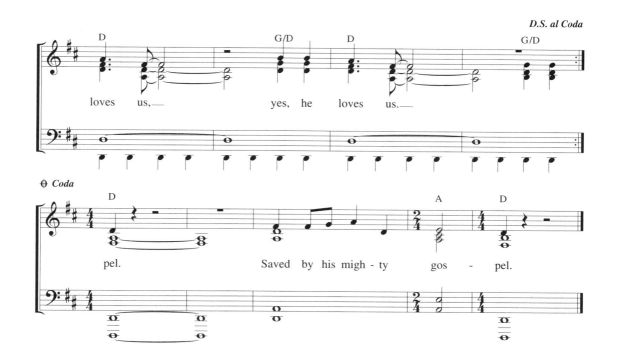

*D.S. al Coda*

loves us, ___ yes, he loves us.

Coda

pel. Saved by his migh - ty gos - pel.

# SPRING HARVEST
# song search

If you need help to find a song on a particular theme or Scripture passage, or just want to know which of the Spring Harvest songbooks or albums features the song you're after - use our song search.

» search online at **www.springharvest.org/songsearch**

# 51

# Lord, I come, I confess
## (Lord, I need you)

Key=B♭

Capo 3(G)

Daniel Carson, Kristian Stanfill,
Christy Nockels, Matt Maher & Jesse Reeves

Moderately

Copyright © 2011 sixsteps Music/worshiptogether.com Songs/Sweater Weather Music/Thankyou Music/Valley Of Songs Music/
Adm. by worshiptogether.com Songs excl. UK & Europe, adm. by Kingswaysongs,
a division of David C Cook tym@kingsway.co.uk Used by Permission

_stay._ 'Cause when I can-not stand I'll fall on you,

Je - sus you're my hope and stay. Lord, I

_D.S. al Coda_

⊕ _Coda_

you. You're my one de-fence, my right - eous-ness, O God, how I need

you. _mp_ My one de - fence, my right - eous - ness, O

God, how I need you.

# 52

# Lord, my life is an empty cup
## (Just to be with you)

Key=D

Paul Baloche
& Jason Ingram

Moderately ♩ = 84

1. Lord, my          life is___ an emp-ty cup,___          here's my
   come to___ the end     of___ me,___          and there's

heart, would___ you fill me___ up?___          I'm face to   the
no-thing___ I have   to___ bring.          But you said   I   be-

ground,     for-sak-ing___ my_____ pride,          leav-ing___ my
long,       you say   I___ am___ yours;___          no-thing___ com-

*v.1 only*

will,   my bur-dens___ be-hind.          more.   All I___ want,___
pares     to know-ing___ you

Copyright © 2009 Integrity Worship Music/ Leadworship Songs/Adm. by EMICMGPublishing.com, excl. UK admin. by Kingswaysongs,
a division of David C Cook tym@kingsway.co.uk  &  Sony Atv Timber Pub Used by Permission

# 53

# Lord, you hear the cry
## (Lord, have mercy)

Key=B♭

Geraldine Latty

Copyright © 2011 Geraldine Latty
www.geraldinelatty.com Used by Permisison

out in lo - ving. Lord, have mer - cy on

**(three times)**

us, Lord, have mer - cy on us.

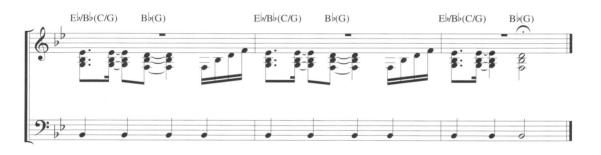

# Return to the Lord

*from Malachi 3*

When we have turned aside from God's ways,
let us hear God say:
**Return to me, and I will return to you.**

When we have held back from giving generously,
let us hear God say:
**Return to me, and I will return to you.**

When we have questioned God's fairness,
let us hear God say:
**Return to me, and I will return to you.**

Return to me, says the living God,
for I am patient and ready to forgive.
And all God's people say:
**Amen.**

168

© 2010 Mark Earey

# May the life that flows from you flow in me
## (Bringing the world to life)

# 54

Key=A♭

Fran Pratt

Copyright © 2010 Mercy/Vineyard Publishing/Admin by Song Solutions CopyCare
www.songsolutions.org Used by Permission

love that pours from you____ pour out____ of me.____
be your voice,____ speak-ing grace__ and peace.____

**Chorus**

You're bring - ing__ the world to life,____ show-ing__ us

what it means__ to live;____ in you__ we live and move and

breathe, you are bring-ing__ the world to life.____

2. May I O Je - sus,

*Last time to Coda*

*D.C. (v.2)* | *2.* **Mid section**

# 55

# Nothing can tear us
## (Furious)

With energy

Key=C

Jeremy Riddle

Copyright © 2011 Mercy/Vineyard Publishing/Admin by Song Solutions CopyCare
www.songsolutions.org Used by Permission

We were really excited to have the chance to record this song for "FRESH: New Songs for the Church"!

# Top tips for leading worship using action songs

### by Doug Horley

Firstly it's important to acknowledge that children of all ages really can worship. Psalm 8 verse 2 says "From the lips of children and infants you have ordained praise…". How amazing is that! God wants children of all ages to praise and worship him. Our job is to help them do just that. What a privilege!

We journey with children in worship. To see children go deep in their worship takes time. Some children have very short attention spans and unless what we do at the start of the journey is fun and engaging there's every chance they won't get on board with us. That's where action songs are good – they help the children get on board. Here are a few top tips to help you…

### Practice
Worship leading is a skill and skill develops through practice. Spend time learning the actions before you have a go at doing the song with the children.

### Be dynamic!
If you stand at the front and look like a wet Wednesday then don't be surprised if the children all look the same! Throw yourself into it 100% and ask the rest of the children's leaders to join you. It's important that the whole team realises they are role models for the children. Get a couple of the team (or children) to help lead the actions with you at the front so you're not on your own!

### Use CDs or DVDs
These are a great way to lead worship as a) you can control the volume of the music and b) you don't have to be a great singer! DVDs add a great visual element and often have the words on the screen as well.

### Use an instrument
I haven't found a way to play guitar and do the actions at the same time (!) so if you play an instrument get some of the team to do the actions with you. If you don't play then see if you can involve your adult worship leader and utilise their skills. Get them to play and sing while you and some of the children's team sing and do the actions.

### Don't make it too long!
Two or three faster songs and then a quieter song can make for a great worship time.

### No big gaps
Don't have big gaps between the songs as you'll lose the children's attention quickly.

### Do fewer songs more often
It takes time for children to learn actions and the first time I do an action song with them they sometimes don't sing. If you sing the song a few times over a period of weeks they'll get to know the song and will start singing along. When you hear them, encourage them by saying, "That sounds great boys and girls, can you sing a bit louder?" It's amazing how effective that is!

### Space to pray
The end of a quiet song is a great place to pause and pray over the children and to ask the Holy Spirit to come and speak to them. I keep that quiet moment going by playing some chords on an instrument in the same key as the song or by playing an instrumental CD track.

And finally…

### Have fun! Go for it!

*Doug Horley*
*www.duggiedugdug.co.uk*

# 56 Now may the peace of the Lord
## (The peace)

Key=E♭

Graham Kendrick

Capo 3(C)

Flowing ♪ = 120

Copyright © 2010 Make Way Music www.grahamkendrick.co.uk
International copyright secured. All rights reserved. Used by Permission

There's a beautiful acoustic arrangement of this song on "FRESH: New Songs for the Church".

# 57

# O precious sight
## (The wonder of the cross)

Key=A♭

Capo 1(G)

Vicky Beeching

Steadily

Copyright © 2007 Thankyou Music/Adm. by worshiptogether.com Songs excl. UK & Europe, adm. by Kingswaysongs,
a division of David C Cook tym@kingsway.co.uk  Used by permission

ne - ver lose the won-der, the won - der of the cross. May I see it like the

first time, standing as a sin - ner lost. Un-done by mer - cy and left

speech - less, watch ing wide - eyed at the cost.—— May I ne - ver lose the

*(Fine)*

won - der, the won - der of the cross. 3. Be - hold, the

*D.C. al fine*

# 58 O the deep, deep love of Jesus

Key=E♭m

Samuel Trevor Francis (1834-1925)
Arr. Calvin Hollingworth
Piano adpt. David Ball

Capo 1(Dm)
Stately

1. O the deep, deep love of Jesus,
2. O the deep, deep love of Jesus
3. O the deep, deep love of Jesus,

vast, un - mea - sured, bound - less, free!
spread his praise from shore to shore!
love of ev - 'ry love the best!

Rol - ling as a migh - ty o - cean
How he lov - eth, e - ver lov - eth
'Tis an o - cean full of bles - sing,

in its full - ness o - ver me!
chang - eth ne - ver, ne - ver - more!
'tis a ha - ven giv - ing rest!

Copyright © 2011 Song Solutions Daybreak
www.songsolutions.org Used by Permission

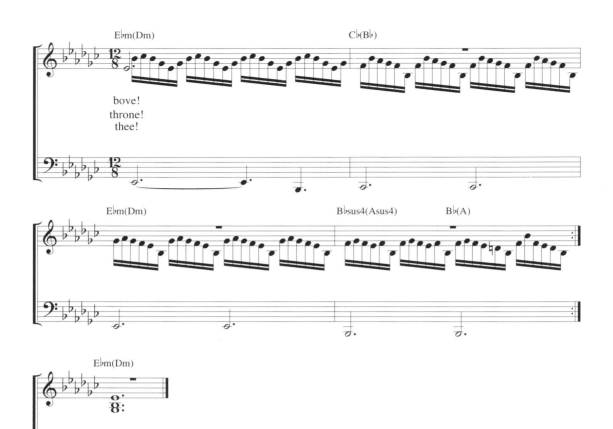

bove!
throne!
thee!

Even *there*
*your* hand will
*guide* me,
*your*
right hand
will **hold** me **fast**

*Psalm 139:10*

# O, the blood

# 59

Key=G

Thomas Miller
& Mary Beth Miller

Freely; building

1. O, the blood, crim-son love, price of life's de-mand;
2. Sa-viour Son, ho-ly One, slain so I can live;
3. O, what love, no great-er love, grace, how can it be

— shame-ful sin placed on him, the hope—
O, see the Lamb, the great I AM, who takes—
that in my sin, yes, e-ven then, he shed

— of ev-'ry man.
— a-way my sin.
— his blood for me.

**Chorus** O, the blood of Je-sus wash-es me, O, the

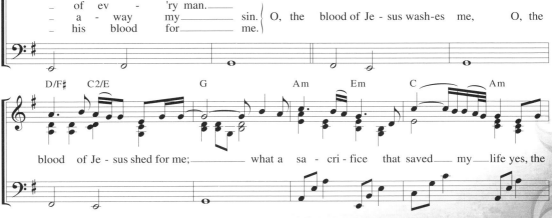

blood of Je-sus shed for me; what a sa-cri-fice that saved my life yes, the

Copyright © 2010 Thomas Miller/Mary Beth Miller/Gateway Create Publishing/Integrity's Praise! Music/Adm. by EMICMGPublishing.com, excl. UK admin. by Kingswaysongs, a division of David C Cook tym@kingsway.co.uk Used by Permission

# Prayer of confession

You speak to us in the language of love,
**Forgive us where we have taken that love for granted.**

You speak to us in the language of redemption,
**Forgive us where we have ignored your sacrifice.**

You speak to us in the language of renewal,
**Forgive us where we have preferred our old ways.**

You speak to us in the language of truth,
**Forgive us where we have been deceitful.**

You speak to us in the language of faithfulness,
**Forgive us where we have been disbelieving.**

Lord, let us hear your Word afresh today,
**And help us learn to speak your language. Amen.**

*© 2011 Marie Birkinshaw*

# 60

# Oh, the Lord, our strength and song
## (Song of Moses)

Key=G

Chris Moerman, Pat Barrett, Ben Smith,
Aaron Keyes & Graham Kendrick

Flowing

1. Oh, the Lord, our strength and song; high-est praise to him be-
storms of hell pur-sue, in dark-est night we wor-ship
saints and an-gels bow, hosts of hea-ven are cry-ing

longs. Christ the Lord, the con-qu'ring King, your name we
you. You di-vide the ra-ging sea; from death to
out, 'Glo-ry, glo-ry to the King. You reign for

raise, your tri-umphs Praise the sing. Praise the
life you safe-ly lead.
all e-ter-ni-ty.'

Copyright © 2010 Thankyou Music/Adm. by worshiptogether.com Songs excl. UK & Europe, adm. by Kingswaysongs,
a division of David C Cook tym@kingsway.co.uk & Itisreal Music.Com/Barrett Daddy Music/Flock Street Music/
EMICMG & Make Way Music www.grahamkendrick.co.uk Used by Permission

# On that day, there will be no injustice
## (On that day)

Steady gospel feel

Key=A

Geraldine Latty

1. On that day,_____ there will be no__ in-jus - tice; on that day,—
   (2.)__ there will be no__ more sick - ness; on that day,—
   (3.)__ there'll be no he - si - ta - tion; on that day,—

— there will be no__ more poor.__ there will be no__ more death.__ So to - day—
— ev - 'ry - one will wor - ship you.__

— I will love,— I will live,— I will work,— I will join in— to see— your

king - dom come. 2. On that day,— come. Je - sus, thank you for the

Copyright © 2007 Thankyou Music/Adm. by worshiptogether.com Songs excl. UK & Europe, adm. by Kingswaysongs,
a division of David C Cook tym@kingsway.co.uk  Used by permission

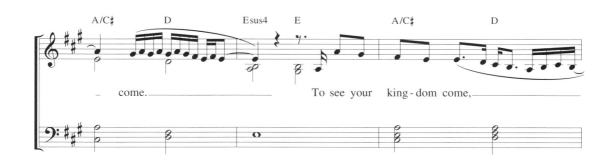

come. To see your king - dom come,

**Tag**

Hal - le - lu - jah. Hal - le - lu - jah,

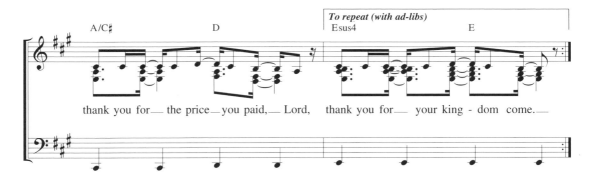

*To repeat (with ad-libs)*

thank you for the price you paid, Lord, thank you for your king - dom come.

*Last time*
Esus4

# 62 Only one name

Key=A

Pete James

Capo 2(G)

Moderate rock feel

1. On-ly one name, strong e-nough to save;
one name spans the breadth of time,

— on-ly one name, o-ver-comes the grave.
— on-ly one name, hu-man and di-vine.

— On-ly one name, is the hope of all the earth;
— On-ly one name, to whom ev-'ry knee will bow:

— ri-sen Sa-viour, he is Je-sus.
— King of hea-ven, he is Je-sus.

Copyright © 2011 Song Solutions Daybreak
www.songsolutions.org Used by Permission

# SPRING HARVEST
# song search

If you need help to find a song on a particular theme or Scripture passage, or just want to know which of the Spring Harvest songbooks or albums features the song you're after - use our song search.

» search online at **www.springharvest.org/songsearch**

**because kids deserve the best**
www.elevationmusic.com/elevationkids

**Spring Harvest**

# KIDS PRAISE PARTY DVD

**Features**
10 cartoon
worship songs with:
· sing-along karaoke ·
· subtitles ·
· sign language ·
· backing tracks ·

A fantastic new animated DVD which contains 10 cartoon songs. The perfect high energy resource for church, school or home, designed to bring kids the great news of Jesus in a relevant and fun way.

**FEATURES:** 10 cartoon worship songs with sing-along karaoke, subtitles, sign language and backing tracks.

**DISCOVER MORE FROM ELEVATION KIDS HERE**

**Available from EssentialChristian.com or your local Christian bookstore**

**essential christian**

# 63

# Our God is stronger

Key=A

Pete James
& Chris Davies

Copyright © 2010 Song Solutions Daybreak
www.songsolutions.org Used by Permission

# 64

# Our hearts will not forget
## (Now is the time for us)

Key=B♭

Capo 3(G)

Luke Hellebronth,
Martyn Layzell & Oliver Snelling

Positively

1. Our hearts will not for-get___ all of your pro-mi-ses,___
2. We're dar-ing to be-lieve,___ trust-ing in what's un-seen,___

_ your words are___ truth.___ Out of the wil-der-ness___
_ by faith, we'll___ see.___ You're light-ing up the night,___

*(Small notes v.2)*

we run in-to your___ grace,___ you've set us___ free;___ we won't_
new hope that shines so___ bright,___ e-ter-nal-ly;___ and we won't_

_ turn back,___ you're the on — ly way.___ Now is the time for__ us_
_ turn back,___ you're the on — ly way.___

_ to sing of your great___ love,___ we wor-ship you, God,___ for-e-ver you, God.___

Copyright © 2011 Thankyou Music/Adm. by worshiptogether.com Songs excl. UK & Europe, adm. by kingswaysongs.com, a division of David C Cook tym@kingsway.co.uk Used by Permission.

We hear you cal - ling— us,——— to show the world your— love,—

*Last time to Coda*

— the sound— of free - dom— will be— our an - them.———

*D.C. (v.2)*

*D.S.S. al Coda*

We sing it— out.——

# From the Church, for the Church

Our slogan 'From the Church, for the Church' sums up what Vineyard worship has always been about – giving it away. When John Wimber established the Vineyard movement of churches in the late 70s, 'giving it away' was his key reforming message when it came to demonstrating the Gospel. He understood deeply that as believers we are called to give everything we have to the Kingdom because, after all, that's what Jesus' ministry was all about.

And this extended not just to ministry but also to worship. Over the years Vineyard worship has been grounded in the simple expression of our love for our Lord. To lead worship, it was not a pre-requisite that you had to be an accomplished musician nor that you had to have the best band of musicians to make it work. The early worship leaders were almost always people who simply had a passion to worship and almost by default got into leading others in it – and then learnt the craft!

This deliberate simplicity was at the very core of its accessibility and allowed us to give it away and replicate it throughout the modern church. Vineyard worship has influenced and affected the church worldwide in a way that even 30 years later the majority of today's songwriters and leaders will point back to a Vineyard worship song or songwriter and talk of how they were influenced and released into what they're doing today.

There are three core values that underpin Vineyard worship, namely 'Integrity, Accessibility and Intimacy'.

The first is all about doing what we do truthfully and with a sense of the deep calling of leading worship. If we lead out of a sense of duty or from a desire to become rich and famous, then we're not leading from a value of integrity. We have come across many people who are extremely gifted musicians, but they've chosen to stay in the Kingdom and forego the trappings of the secular music industry to serve their local church, understanding what music is really for.

Accessibility allows everyone to worship to a particular song. When we receive song submissions, one of the judgment criteria is 'Can and will your regular church attendee be able to easily follow the song and worship with it?' However original the song might be, if the melody is too complicated or the lyrics too wordy, we will reject the song on that basis. Our goal is always to want regular worshippers to be able to worship, not become spectators of a performance. Worship is not for observation but participation.

Intimacy is the primary call of God. It is where we meet with God in a personal, meaningful and often transforming way. This is difficult to define – what stirs my soul is probably very different to another person, but we realise we must keep in the mainstream of popular culture. So the point here is that we 'give it away', meet people in their culture and encourage the younger generations to write songs and lead their peers in an intimate expression of worship.

'From the Church, for the Church' embodies the Vineyard approach of documenting (through the recording of songs) what God has given his Church and then releasing it to the wider body (via CD, download and events). We seek to give of our best whilst at the same time not becoming exclusive – isn't that what Jesus taught us to do?

*Chris Whitelock*
*www.vineyardrecords.co.uk*

# Rise up

65

Key=G

Words: Nigel Briggs
Music: Trent

Country rock ♩ = 133

**Verse** G

1. Rise up,— rise up,— there's a new day com-ing; his love,— his love—

Csus2

— through the na - tions run-ning, he can fill your heart,— he can fill your

(v.2)

G

soul.— Come and see,— come and see—
2. Reach out,— reach out,—

— that the old has gone,— his light— his truth— now for ev-'ry-
— 'cause he is here,— free-dom— through grace— now is ev-'ry-

Copyright © 2011 Trent www.trentband.com
Used by Permission

We recorded a stripped-down arrangment of this song for the acoustic CD of "FRESH: New Songs for the Church". We hope you like it!

# 66

# Spirit come

Key=C

Nick J. Drake
& Becky Drake

Prayerfully

**Chorus**

Spi - rit come, breathe on us we pray.

Ev - 'ry part of me in need of you; Spi - rit come. come. O -

- pen our hearts, o - pen our minds to you; o - pen our hearts, o - pen our minds to

you. Lead us through the day, guide us through the night; Spi - rit of the

*1st time D.C.*

Lord.

*(1° omit L.H.)*

Copyright © 2011 Thankyou Music/Adm. by worshiptogether.com Songs excl. UK & Europe, adm. by kingswaysongs.com,
a division of David C Cook tym@kingsway.co.uk Used by Permission.

Breathe on_____ us,____ Spi - rit of God._____

Come__ like__ a fire,_____ burn__ like__ a flame,_____ o - pen our hearts__

__ for more of you a - gain._____ Come__ like__ a fire,____ burn__ like__ a flame,__

__ o - pen our hearts____ for more of you a - gain.__ Come like a fire,__

(small notes 2°&3°)

# 67

## Stand up, come on, stand your ground
### (Stand up)

Capo 2(Em)

Key=F#m

Graham Kendrick

1. Stand up, come on, stand your ground.
2. Speak up, come on, make some noise,

Stand up, come on, don't back down.
cry out, where they have no voice;

Rise up, come on, side by side.
for jus - tice, come on fight to win.
Lift up, ho - nour Jes - us' name,

Wake up, come on, don't stand by.
for mer - cy, come on mus - cle in.
look up, ne - ver be a - shamed.

Copyright © 2009 Make Way Music www.grahamkendrick.co.uk
International copyright secured. All rights reserved. Used by Permission

Verse

F#m/E (Em/D)

3. Hands up, come on ho - ly hands,

Dmaj9(C)

B/D#(A/C#)

join up, pray - ing 'cross the land.

D.S.S. al Coda 1    Coda 1
D2(C)

Ev - 'ry - bo - dy stand up, ev - 'ry - bo - dy stand up,

D.S. (with repeat) al Coda 2

ev - 'ry - bo - dy stand up, stand up and fight___

Coda 2
D2(C)                    F#m7(Em)          Tag
                                           F#m(Em)

___ let's take some ground.___ Our God is strong to save;

our God is strong to save.

Our God is strong to save; our God is

strong to save.

When these things
begin to take place,

*stand up* and
*lift* up your heads,

because your
*redemption*
*is*
*drawing near*

*Luke 21:28*

# 68

# Standing on this mountain top
## (Never once)

Key=B

Matt Redman, Jason Ingram
& Tim Wanstall

Capo 4(G)

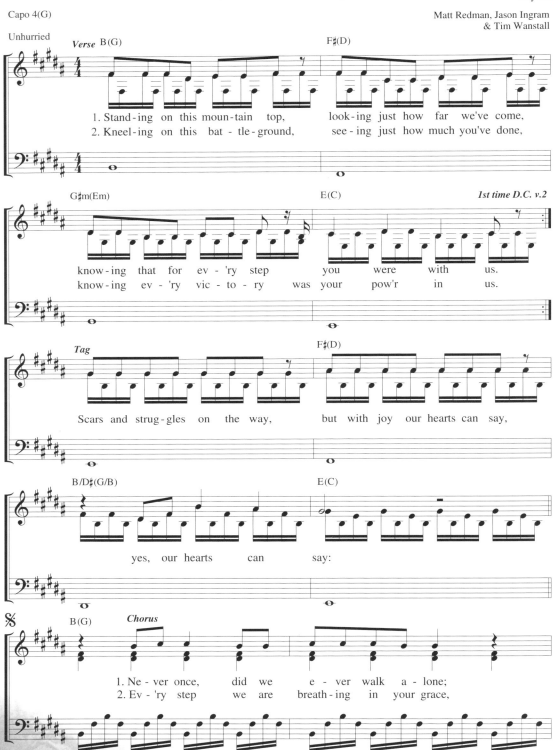

1. Stand-ing on this moun-tain top, look-ing just how far we've come,
2. Kneel-ing on this bat-tle-ground, see-ing just how much you've done,

know-ing that for ev-'ry step you were with us.
know-ing ev-'ry vic-to-ry was your pow'r in us.

Scars and strug-gles on the way, but with joy our hearts can say,

yes, our hearts can say:

1. Ne - ver once, did we e - ver walk a - lone;
2. Ev - 'ry step we are breath-ing in your grace,

Copyright © 2011 Thankyou Music/Said And Done Music/Adm. by worshiptogether.com Songs excl. UK & Europe, adm. by Kingswaysongs, a division of David C Cook tym@kingsway.co.uk & Chrysalis Music Ltd & Sony ATV Timber Publishing Used by Permission

# Take these hands
## (All I am)

Key=A
Phil Wickham

1. Take these hands, I know they're emp-ty, but with you they can
2. Take these feet, I know they stum-ble, but you use the weak,
3. Take this heart, set it on fi-re, shin-ing in the dark,

be used for beau-ty in your per-fect plan;— all I am is yours.—
you use the hum-ble, so please use me;— all I am is yours.—
I want to tell the world of who you are;—

**D.C. (v.2)** | **2.,3.** (v.3)
all I am is yours.—

all I am is yours.— I give you

**Chorus**

(ch.2)
(1.) all my life, I'm let-ting it go,— a liv-ing sa-cri-fice, no
(2.) ev-'ry-thing, to you I be-long,— ev-'ry beat of my heart, the

Copyright © 2011 Phil Wickham Music, Seems Like Music/Simpleville Music/Small Stone Media BV, Holland/
Adm by Song Solutions Daybreak www.songsolutions.org Used by Permission

Last time to Coda ⊕  1.

lon - ger my own;___ all I am___ is yours,___ all I am___ is yours.___
breath in my lungs;___ all I am___ is yours, all I am___

D.C.(v.3)

A        Bm7        F♯m7        D

2.,4.        D.S. (ch.2) (al Coda)  3.

___ is yours.___ I give you ___ is yours.___

**Mid section**

D        A        F♯m7

I lift my hands up;     God I sur - ren - der     all that I am for your glo -

E        D        A

- ry, your ho - nour, your fame.     I lift my hands up;     God, I sur - ren - der to you.___

I give you

is yours.

# 70

# The broken, have come to the Mender
## (The broken)

Key=E

Mark Robins

Moderate, open feel

The bro - ken,— have come to the Men - der,—
have come to the Ma - ker,— have come to you;—
ap - proach - ing— your throne of grace,—
here in this place, yearn - ing.—
On - ly— you are— a -

Copyright © 2009 Mark Robins Music/Rain Music
Used by Permission

# The heavens, horizons of this earth
## *(Far greater)*

# 71

Capo 3(C)

Key=E♭

Rich White

Positively

**Verse** Cm(Am)       A♭(F)       E♭(C)

The hea - vens,＿＿＿ ho - ri - zons of＿ this earth
na - ture,＿＿＿ the sci - ence of＿ this world＿

B♭/D(G/B)       Fm7(Dm)       Cm(Am)

＿ can - not con - tain＿＿ you, my God.＿
＿ can - not re - strain＿＿ you, my God.＿

B♭(G)    *1.*      *2.*      A♭(F)   **Bridge**

＿＿ All＿ Un -

B♭/A♭(G)   A♭maj7(F)   B♭(G)      E♭/G(C/E)      A♭(F)

ri - valled, be - yond e - qual,＿＿＿ you are

Copyright © 2010 Thankyou Music/Adm. by worshiptogether.com Songs excl. UK & Europe, adm. by kingswaysongs.com, a division of David C Cook tym@kingsway.co.uk Used by Permission.

# 72

# The Lord is here among us
## (Forever reign)

Key=B

Capo 4(G)

Claire Hamilton
& David Ostby

With an ambient feel

1. The Lord is here— a-mong— us, our for-tress and— our shield;— a
Lord is here— a-mong— us, our for-tress and— our shield;— a

God who gives— us shel-ter from the storm.— The
God who gives— us cou-rage in the fight.— The

Lord is here— a-mong— us, de-pen-da-ble— and good;— a
Lord is here— a-mong— us, a-vail-a-ble— and true;— a

God who's known as faith-ful till the end.— Our
God whose name is wor-thy to be praised.—

Copyright © 2010 Thankyou Music/Adm. by worshiptogether.com Songs excl. UK & Europe, adm. by kingswaysongs.com,
a division of David C Cook tym@kingsway.co.uk Used by Permission.

# Recorded teaching from Spring Harvest 2012

**Available on CD, DVD\* and USB MP3 Stick**
\*DVD of main meetings only

Exclusively available from
EssentialChristian.com

# 73 The perfect wisdom of our God

Key=B♭

Capo 3(G)

Stuart Townend
& Keith Getty

Moderately
*Verse*

1. The per-fect wis-dom of our God, re-vealed in all the u-ni-verse: all things cre-a-ted by his hand, and held to-ge-ther at his com-mand. He knows the my-st'ries of the seas, the se-crets of the stars are

match-less wis-dom of his ways that mark the path of right-eous-ness; his word a lamp un-to my feet, his Spi-rit teach-ing and guid-ing me. And O the mys-t'ry of the cross, that God should suf-fer for the

grant me wis-dom from a-bove, to pray for peace and cling to love, and teach me hum-bly to re-ceive the sun and rain of your sov-'reign-ty. Each strand of sor-row has a place with-in this ta-pes-try of

Copyright © 2011 Thankyou Music/Adm. by worshiptogether.com Songs excl. UK & Europe, adm. by Kingswaysongs,
a division of David C Cook tym@kingsway.co.uk & Getty Music info@gettymusic.com Used by Permission

his;    he guides the pla - nets on their way, and turns the
lost, so that the fool might shame the wise and all the
grace; so through the trials I choose to say: 'Your per - fect

earth through a - no - ther day.
glo - ry might go to
will in your per - fect

2. The way. Each Christ.

*Last time to Coda*

*1.,2. (repeat as required after v.3)*

3. O

# 74

# There is no love
## (I surrender)

Key=C

Kim Walker-Smith & Justin Byrne

Copyright © 2010 Jesus Culture Music
All rights reserved Admin by Jesus Culture Music Used by Permission

# 75

# There's a dance
## (Dance of our God)

Key=C#m

Capo 4 (Am)
With a reggae rhythm

Geraldine Latty & busbee

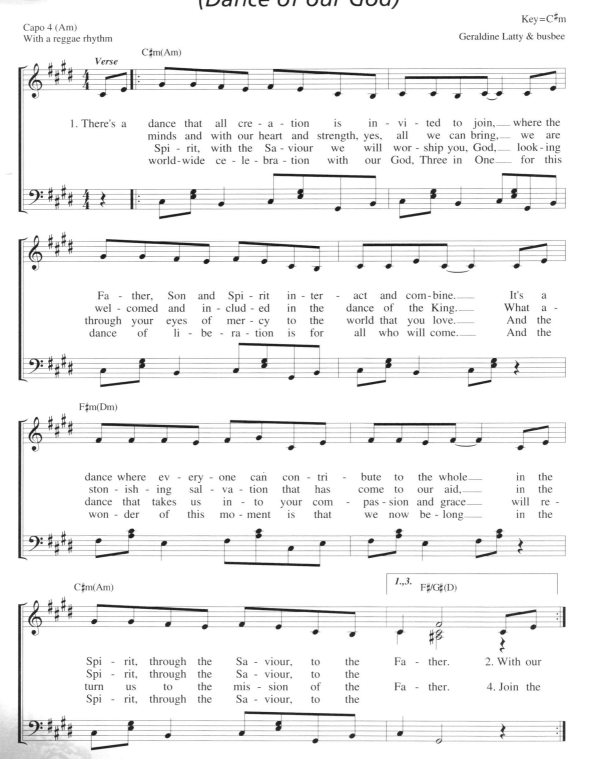

1. There's a dance that all cre-a-tion is in-vi-ted to join,___ where the Father, Son and Spi-rit in-ter-act and com-bine.___ It's a dance where ev-ery-one can con-tri-bute to the whole___ in the Spi-rit, through the Sa-viour, to the Fa-ther. 2. With our

minds and with our heart and strength, yes, all we can bring,___ we are wel-comed and in-clud-ed in the dance of the King.___ What a-ston-ish-ing sal-va-tion that has come to our aid,___ in the Spi-rit, through the Sa-viour, to the Fa-ther. 4. Join the

Spi-rit, with the Sa-viour we will wor-ship you, God,___ look-ing through your eyes of mer-cy to the world that you love.___ And the dance that takes us in-to your com-pas-sion and grace___ will re-turn us to the mis-sion of the Fa-ther.

world-wide ce-le-bra-tion with our God, Three in One___ for this dance of li-be-ra-tion is for all who will come.___ And the won-der of this mo-ment is that we now be-long___ in the Spi-rit, through the Sa-viour, to the

C#m(Am)

F#m(Dm)

C#m(Am)

*1.,3.* F#/G#(D)

Copyright © 2005 Thankyou Music & The Livingstone Collective/Adm. by worshiptogether.com Songs excl. UK & Europe, adm. by Kingswaysongs, a division of David C Cook tym@kingsway.co.uk Used by Permission

Fa-ther. La la la la la la la la, la la la la la la la la. La la la

la la la la la, la la la la la la la la. This is the
*(This is the*

dance full of glo-ri-ous di-ver-si-ty. This is the
*dance in the my-s'try of the Tri-ni-ty.)*

dance of our God. (3. In the)

# 76

# This is the dream
## (No chains on me)

Key=E

Chris Tomlin, Matt Redman
& Jesse Reeves

Moderate rock

Copyright © 2010 Thankyou Music/worshiptogether.com Songs/sixsteps Music/Vamos Publishing/Said and Done Music/Adm. by worshiptogether.com Songs
excl. UK & Europe, adm. by Kingswaysongs, a division of David C Cook tym@kingsway.co.uk Used by Permission

my way,___ my heart is___ free,___ no chains on___ me.___

**1.,3.**   ***Last time to Coda*** 🌐   E

**D.C.(v.2)** | **2.**   E

2. Now is the time,___   ___

*(Continues. . .)*

**Mid section**

Whoa,___ whoa,___ whoa,_____whoa,_____whoa.____ (The)

*2° 8va*   **1.**

walls   are com-ing down,         the   walls are com-ing down.       The

*(Small notes optional rhythm.... etc.)*

The walls are com-ing down, the walls are com-ing down.

*D.S. al Coda* ⊕ *Coda*

Like a rol-

# God is great among the nations *from Malachi 1:11*

From beginning to end
**you are great among the nations.**

From daybreak to nightfall
**you are great among the nations.**

From east to west
**you are great among the nations.**

Great God of many nations, of all times and all places,
accept the offering of our strength and our weakness,
our beginnings and our endings,
our youth and our age,
to be used to bring your rule in this world
and your eternal reign nearer, day by day.
**Amen.**

*© 2010 Mark Earey*

# 77

# Undivided love

Key=G

Ben Cantelon
& Martyn Layzell

Steadily

1. Un - di - vi - ded love I bring to you, You've be - come my
2. Un - di - vi - ded love you gave it all, lay - ing down your

ev - 'ry - thing; grace sings out its song, now I re -
ma - je - sty. Mer - cy made a way, called me by

- spond, lift - ing up this of - fer - ing. I give you my life
- name, wel - comed me with o - pen arms. I give you my life

Lord, you take con - trol; you have my heart, my soul.

*D.C.(v.2)* my soul. I give you my life

Pre-chorus

Copyright © 2011 Thankyou Music/Adm. by worshiptogether.com Songs excl. UK & Europe, adm. by kingswaysongs.com,
a division of David C Cook tym@kingsway.co.uk Used by Permission.

Lord, you take con-trol;—— you have my heart,—— my soul.—

'Cause it's all for you,——

all that I am,— I sur-ren - der— Je - sus, all for you,——

Sa - viour, to you— I sur-ren - der now, I sur-ren - der
'Cause it's

now.

*Chorus*

*(Small notes for last chorus repeat (D.S.))*

*Last time to Coda*

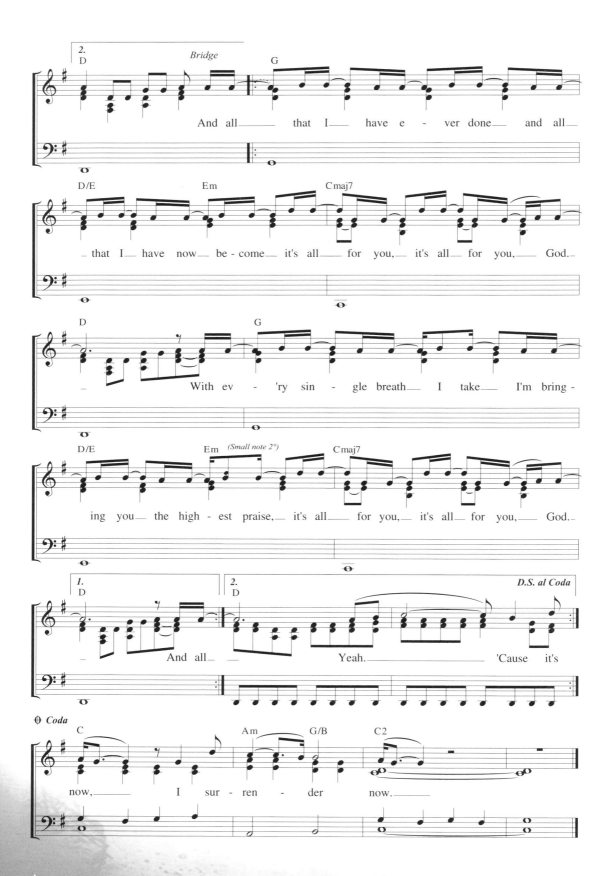

# 78

# We call to you, the living God
## (In your presence)

Key=C

Moderately

Stuart Barbour
& Becky Frith

1. We call to you,_____ the liv-ing God,_____
come and drink;_____

and turn our eyes_____ to find your face;_____
for all in need_____ are wel - comed in._____

we long to live_____ close to you,_____
Tears of pain_____ are washed a - way,_____

with - in the depths_____ of your love._____
lives are healed_____ for God is here._____

Copyright © 2011 Song Solutions Daybreak
www.songsolutions.org Used by Permission

be here with you___ in your pre - sence, Lord.___

2. To all who thirst,___ Our

# SPRING HARVEST
## *s* **ng** search

If you need help to find a song on a particular theme or Scripture passage, or just want to know which of the Spring Harvest songbooks or albums features the song you're after - use our song search.

» search online at *www.springharvest.org/songsearch*

245

# 79 We have come to worship

Key=E
Pete James
Capo 4(C)

Worshipfully

We have come to wor - ship,—— we have come to bow—down,—

we have come to love—— you,—— and

bring the high-est praise, bring the high-est praise.——

Copyright © 2011 Song Solutions Daybreak
www.songsolutions.org Used by Permission

# 80 We have heard a joyful sound
## (We have heard a joyful sound (He saves))

Key=B♭

Words: Priscilla Owens
Music: William Kirkpatrick
Additional words and music: Colin Webster

Capo 3(G)

Passionately

1. We have heard a joyful sound Jesus saves!
2. Sing above the battle's strife, Jesus saves!
3. Give the winds a mighty voice, Jesus saves!

Spread the tidings all around Jesus saves!
By his death and endless life, Jesus saves!
Let the nations now rejoice, Jesus saves!

Bear the news to ev'ry land, climb the steeps and cross the waves.
Sing it softly through the gloom, when the heart for mercy craves.
Shout salvation full and free, highest hills and deepest caves.

Onwards! It's our Lord's command: Jesus saves!
Sing in triumph o'er the tomb: Jesus saves! He
This our song of victory: Jesus saves!

Copyright © 2011 Colin Webster Cornerstone Worship
www.cornerstoneworship.co.uk Used by Permission

saves, he saves, Christ Je - sus is a - live; his

cross and grave, be - come our vic - t'ry cry. He

saves, he saves, be re - con - ciled to God; tell the

*Last time to Coda*

nat - ions: Je - sus saves!_____

*D.C. (v.2.,3.) al Coda*

# We were once in darkness
## (Once in darkness)

Capo 2(D)

Key=E

Rock ♩ = 144

Luke Hellebronth,
Beth Croft & David Gate

Verse

A(G)　F♯m(Em)

1. We were once in dark - ness,
and hurt - ing,

liv - ing in
to a peo -

C♯m(Bm)　A(G)　F♯m(Em)

_ the sha - dows,
- ple search - ing,

you came to us,
we will tell the world,

C♯m(Bm)

(Small notes v.2)

our shin - ing light.
you're the shin - ing light.

When the night
There is hope

(v.2)

A(G)　F♯m(Em)　C♯m(Bm)

_ was end - less,
_ and free - dom,

and the world was wait - ing,
to be found in you,

A(G)　F♯m(Em)

you came for us,
we will show the world,

our shin -
you're the shin -

Copyright © 2011 Luke Hellebronth, Beth Croft, David Gate
Used by Permission

# 82 We'll live as you have called us
## (True praise)

Key=G

Tim Neeves & Mairi Neeves

Thoughtfully ♩ = 68

1. We'll live as you have called us,
2. We'll break the chains of in-jus-tice,

with hearts that break for the poor,
and hun-ger for your ways,

re-leas-ing hea-vy bur-dens, we'll set the cap-tives free;
we'll pour out love for the weak and the wea-ry; we will a-rise,

they shall go free.
your church a-rise.

Copyright © 2011 PushMusicPublishing/Administered by Amos3music.
info@amos3music.com Used by Permission

Then our light will a-rise, and your glo - ry will shine through us,

then our light will a-rise.

We will know your pre - sence, we will trust

your heal - ing, we will feel your plea - sure o - ver us.

As we — walk — in your foot - steps, as we — build —

Your king - dom, we will — bring — true praise — as you — de - serve,

as you — de - serve.

now is the time — to bring — true — praise. —

now is the time — to bring — true — praise. —

# 83

# *We're in this battle together*
## *(We're coming home)*

Key=B♭

Pete James

Capo 3(G)

Rock ♩ = 124

1. We're in this bat - tle to - ge - ther, I'm not leav - ing with - out you.___ Com - rades in this ad - ven - ture, we stand as one in hope___ and truth.

2. We're liv - ing in an a - wake - ning, the days the pro - phets told are here,___ and with this fire___ with - in us, we'll fill our ci - ty with the love of Je - sus.

You've got my back and I've___ got yours,___ with

Un - til the great and glo - ri - ous day,___ when

Copyright © 2010 Song Solutions Daybreak
www.songsolutions.org Used by Permission

run, run, don't e-ver give in, we're run-ning this race to-ge - ther.

Run, run, don't e-ver look back, we're run - ning this race to - ge -

**1.**
- ther. Come on,

**2.**
- ther. Be - cause

*D.S. al Coda*

*Coda*
- ther.

*Rit.*

# 84

# We're the forgiven
## (We are the free)

Key=B♭

Capo 3(G)

Jonas Myrin
& Matt Redman

Fast rock feel

1. We're the for-gi-ven, sing-ing re-demp-tion's song.
2. We are the ri-sen, liv-ing a-live in you,

There's a fire that burns in-side, a fire
and our pas-sion will not die, no, our pas-

that burns in-side. No-thing can stop us,
-sion will not die. No-thing can stop us,

we'll be run - ning through the night with a fire
we'll be run - ning through the night, and our pas-

that burns in-side, a fire that burns in-side.
-sion will not die, no, our pas - sion will not die.

Copyright © 2011 Thankyou Music/Said And Done Music/Adm. By worshiptogether.com Songs excl. UK & Europe,
adm. by Kingswaysongs, a division of David C Cook tym@kingsway.co.uk
& Jonas Myrin/SHOUT! Publishing/Adm. by Hillsong Publishing publishing@hillsong.com Used by Permission

We like this song so much that we recorded it and put it on "FRESH: New Songs for the Church"!

264

# Ephesians

**Ideal for churches, small groups and individuals looking to explore the book of Ephesians.**

This workbook by Jenny Baker ties in with Spring Harvest 2012.

Available from EssentialChristian.com or your local Christian bookstore

# 85

# We've come here to gather
## *(Hear the sound)*

Key=C

Jonny Grange
& Nigel Briggs

Moderate rock

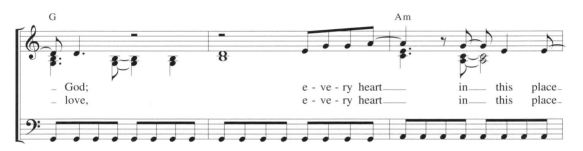

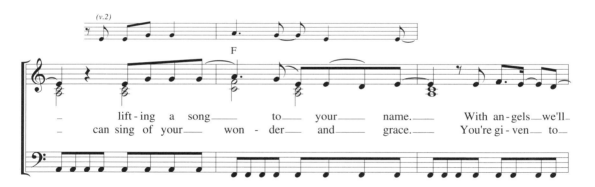

1. We've come here— to ga - ther, for you are— our— God;
mer - cy,— be - cause of— your— love,

e - ve - ry heart— in— this place— lift-ing a song— to— your— name.— With an - gels—we'll
e - ve - ry heart— in— this place— can sing of your— won - der— and— grace.— You're gi - ven— to—

sing, all glo - ry— and ho - nour,
us, a rea - son for liv - ing;—

Copyright © 2010 Vineyard Songs (UK/Eire)/Admin by Song Solutions CopyCare
www.songsolutions.org Used by Permission

*(v.2)*

Am

your po - wer re - leased in this place ___ as we call ___
with free - dom and truth ___ here ___ to - day, ___ as we call ___

F

Am    *Bridge*

___ on ___ your ___ name. ___
___ on ___ your ___ name.

In   a - do - ra - tion, ___

Fm6/A♭

C

___ and   ce - le - bra - tion ___ we   come be - fore ___ you now, ___

F

C    *Chorus*

___ yeah. ___

1. Hear the sound ___ of   our   wor - ship,
2. As   we   look ___ to   your   glo - ry ___

We really enjoyed recording this song for "Fresh: New Songs for the Church"!

# What heart could hold the weight of your love?
## (Holy)

Key=B♭

Matt Redman, Jonas Myrin
& Jason Ingram

Building in intensity

1. What heart could hold the weight of your love, and know the
   lone has pow'r to raise us. Your light will
   come a-gain in glo-ry to judge the

heights of your great worth? What eyes could look on your glo-
shine when all else fades. Our eyes will look on your glo-
liv-ing and the dead. All eyes will look on your glo-

- ri-ous face, shin-ing like the sun? 1. What heart could
- ri-ous face, shin-ing like the sun.
- ri-ous face, shin-ing like the sun.

Who is like you, God? You are

Copyright © 2011 Thankyou Music/Said And Done Music/Adm. by worshiptogether.com Songs excl. UK & Europe, adm. by Kingswaysongs,
a division of David C Cook tym@kingsway.co.uk & Jonas Myrin/SHOUT! Publishing/Hillsong Publishing
publishing@hillsong.com & Sony ATV Timber Publishing Used by Permission

# 87 What love is this that always gives
## (Everlasting love)

Key=D

Stuart Townend
& busbee

Quite slow

1. What love is this that
love is this that
love is this, what

al - ways gives, and ne - ver counts the cost, that beats with - in the
pur - ges fear and can - cels ev - 'ry sin, yet loves e - nough to
price - less gift so free - ly poured on me? If all the wealth of

heart of God with pas - sion for the lost; that lifts me from my
lead me through the fires of dis - ci - pline? The suf - fer - ing that
earth was mine, no rich - er would I be. The great - est prize, to

Copyright © 2011 Thankyou Music & The Livingstone Collective/Adm. byworshiptogether.com Songs excl. UK & Europe,
adm. by Kingswaysongs, a division of David C Cook tym@kingsway.co.uk Used by Permission

# 88 When I stand before your throne
## (Endless hallelujah)

Key=A♭

Matt Redman, Tim Wanstall,
Jonas Myrin & Chris Tomlin
Verse words adapted from hymn "When this passing world is done"
Robert M. McCheyne, 1837

Capo 1(G)

Gently, with awe

1. When I stand be-fore your throne,— dressed in glo-ry— not my own,—
2. I will see you as you are,— love you— with un-sin-ning heart,— and

what a joy— I'll sing— of on— that day.—
see how— much you paid— to bring— me home.—

No more tears or bro-ken dreams,— for-got-ten— is the mi-nor key;
Not till then, Lord,— shall I know,— not till— then, how— much I owe;

*Chorus*

ev-'ry-thing— as it— was meant— to be.— And we will
ev-'ry-thing— I am— be-fore— your throne.—

Copyright © 2011  Thankyou Music/Said And Done Music/Vamos Publishing/worshiptogether.com Songs/sixsteps Music/Adm. by worhiptogether.com
Songs excl. UK & Europe, adm. by Kingswaysongs tym@kingsway.co.uk & Jonas Myrin/SHOUT! Pub./Hillsong Publishing & Chrysalis Music Ltd
Used by Permission

worship, worship. For-e-ver in your pre-sence we will

sing. We will wor-ship, wor-ship you; an

end-less hal-le-lu-jah to the King.

No more

tears, no more shame, no more sin and sor-row e-ver known a-gain.

No more— fears, no more— pain. We will see— you face— to face,— see you face— to face.— And we will—

# *Worship is warfare*

by *Andy Smith*

One of the guys in the youth group explained to me once - "When 'The Christians' moved in, all wearing red hoodies - we thought, they want to live in a rough area, we'll show them what it's like to live in a rough area." The first three years of being on the Eden project in Manchester felt like a huge test of stickability. The young people tried to set our house on fire, they cut the brake cables on the van, they rubbed poo on our front door, urinated through our letter box, wrote my housemate's car off and basically did all they could to test us.

The hardest thing was that they terrorized the church services. They would run in wearing balaclavas, shouting 'naughty' words and shooting people in the bum with BB guns while they were taking communion. Every Sunday they would come in and pretty much riot. For three years, we policed the service like Christian bouncers trying our hardest to curb the disruption without making the young people feel unwanted - tricky.

Inspired by the story of Jehoshaphat, we started a worship meeting called 'Sacred Tent'. We met secretly in another church, worshipped, prayed and wrote down anything we felt God say. As with Jehoshaphat, crazy as it seems, worship is our warfare. We spent a year meeting in secret before God told us to go back to our church to claim back that ground.

As we gathered at church, 'the lads' came over and asked to come in. I thought about smacking them with my guitar, or impaling them with a clarinet, but I said "We're going in here to tell Jesus how much we love him. If you want to do the same, that's cool. If not, we'll see you later". To my shock, they just said "Safe" and went on their way. That night we sang and prayed and declared it as a place where God could be worshipped freely. From that night on, we never had to police the church again. Overnight, God changed the atmosphere in our church and in our community - worship is our warfare.

*Andy Smith*

**Look out for a new album by Andy Smith coming from Elevation in 2012!**

# 89

# When the sun is shining
## (Jesus is my best friend)

Key=A

Vicky Beeching
& Wendy Beech-Ward

Exuberantly

1. When the sun is shin - ing, and I go out to play,
2. When I'm feel - ing lone - ly, when I start to cry,
3. When I leave Spring Har - vest, and some - times life is tough,

I'm so glad that Je - sus
I hear Je - sus whis - per that
I know you're still with me, and

*Chorus*

walks with me all day.
he's right by my side.
your love is e - nough.

Je - sus is my best

friend, Je - sus is my best friend;

Copyright © 2009 Thankyou Music/Adm. by worshiptogether.com Songs excl. UK & Europe,
adm. by Kingswaysongs/Integrity Worship Music/Adm. by EMICMGPublishing.com, excl.
UK admin. by Kingswaysongs, a division of David C Cook tym@kingsway.co.uk Used by Permission

# 90 Who is like the Lord our God?
## (Surprising)

Key=E♭

Capo 3(C)

Geraldine Latty
& busbee

Steady gospel feel

**Verse**

1. Who is like the Lord our God, mov-ing in our lives with sur-
2. God, whose strength holds the u-ni-verse, came to live with us, chose to
3. Ho-ly and sur-pris-ing God, pow-er-ful in truth, vul-n'ra-

pris-ing love? We thought the lion would ov-er-throw,
die our death. We thought that we would pay the price;
ble in love. Your sa-cri-fice will one day be

but saw the Lamb through suf-fring go.
dis-co-vered that you gave your life.
the song that fills e-ter-ni-ty.

**Chorus**

You are the song of yes-ter-day, you are the an-

Copyright © 2005 Thankyou Music & The Livingstone Collective/Adm. byworshiptogether.com Songs excl. UK & Europe,
adm. by Kingswaysongs, a division of David C Cook tym@kingsway.co.uk Used by Permission

them of— to - day.— You're the be - gin - ning and— the end,— the on -

— ly way.— Who can de - fine— your ten - der - ness,— li - mit the pas -

*Last time to Coda* ⊕

— sion of— your grace? You're mag - ni - fi - cent in all your ways.—

*D.C.(v.3)*

*Mid section*

Ho - ly is— the— Lamb of God,—

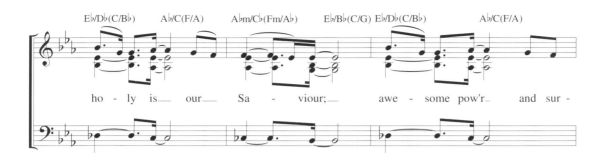

ho-ly is— our— Sa- viour;— awe- some pow'r— and sur-

*D.S. al Coda*

-pri-sing love,— we— are yours— for- e- ver.— You are the song—

℧ *Coda*

ni-fi-cent in all your ways.—

He is before all things, and in Him all things hold together

*Colossians 1:17*

# Who made the ground that I stand on
## (Big, big God)

91

Key=D

Geraldine Latty
& Jonny Hirst

Country feel ♩ = 115

*Verse*

1. Who made the ground that I stand on,
2. Who knows the way that I'm feel-ing,

who made the air that I breathe;
who knows ev-'ry-thing that we need;

what a-bout the sun that helps me see in the day-time, and
who loves e-nough to care for birds in the blue sky,

knows ev-'ry-thing a-bout me? (It's a)
how much more does he care for me?

Copyright © 2009 Geraldine Latty and Jonny Hirst
Used by Permission.

*Chorus*

big, big God who made the world that I stand on, (it's a) big, big God who made the

air that I breath; (it's a) big, big God who made the sun shine down, and it's

*1.*

big, big God who looks af - ter me.

*D.C. (v.2)*

*2.,3.*

*Last time to Coda*

He looks af - ter me.

# 92

# Worship God with the morning sunrise
## (Worship God)

Key=E♭

Geraldine Latty
& busbee

Capo 1(D)

Gospel feel ♩ = 110

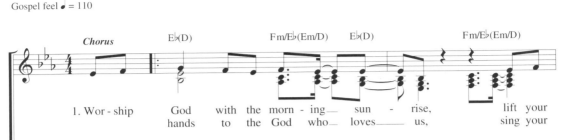

Chorus

1. Wor - ship God with the morn - ing sun - rise, lift your
   hands to the God who loves us, sing your

voice in the eve - ning rain, bring your
song to the One who saves; trust his

Last time to Coda ⊕

thanks and praise, all your ac - co - lades to him.
pro - mi - ses, know that we are his al - ways!

1.

2. Clap your

2.

Verse

1. You are beau - ti - ful - ly dif-
2. We are caught up in your beau-

Copyright © 2005 Thankyou Music & The Livingstone Collective/Adm. byworshiptogether.com songs excl. UK & Europe, adm. by Kingswaysongs,
a division of David C Cook tym@kingsway.co.uk Used by Permission

Trust his pro - mi - ses,__ know that we are his__ al - ways!

**SPRING HARVEST**
**song**search

If you need help to find a song on a particular
theme or Scripture passage, or just want to know
which of the Spring Harvest songbooks or albums
features the song you're after - use our song search.

» search online at **www.springharvest.org/songsearch**

# NO CEILING TO HOPE

## Dangerous Stories of Grace in Action

Servants of Christ are in the transformation business.

This kind of transformation will only happen if we refuse to be seduced by false idols like success, money, fame and security — to be the church we were called to be. We need to take ownership of the problems around us and work with people who are suffering in order to find solutions and offer lasting change. Patrick travels the globe to find examples.

The common element is that in all circumstances Christ is offering hope.

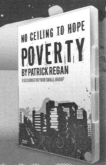

Now available:
NEW Small Group Study DVD

Available from EssentialChristian.com
or your local Christian bookstore

# 93

# You are a refuge
## (Arms)

Key=D
Ben Atkins

Moderately

1. You are a re-fuge for the weak,— an ear to those too crushed to
   those who car-ry pain,— bring burst-ing life to de-sert
   those who stand a-lone, a shel-ter for those with-out a

speak, you pro-mise rest for wea-ry feet, God you— care.
plains, give danc-ing hearts to those in chains, God you— care.
home, e-ve-ry tear that falls you know, God you— care.

2. You car-ry

**Chorus**

1. You have arms that reach the
   arms to reach the

lost and the lone-ly, a heart that loves those with no love at all,—
lost and the lone-ly, hearts to love those with no love at all—

Copyright © RESOUNDworship.org, /Administered by The Jubilate Group
Kitley House, St Katherines Road, Torquay. TQ1 4DE Used by Permission

# 94 You can shine light into the darkness
## (Nothing is impossible)

Vicky Beeching

Key=B

Capo 4(G)

Positively ♩ = 122

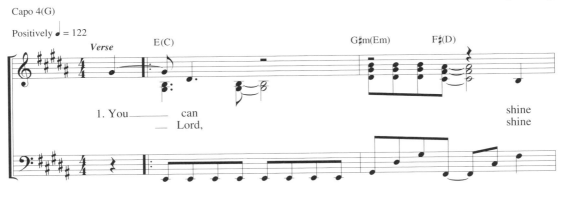

1. You_____ can shine
_____ Lord, shine

light in - to the dark - ness, and you_____ can
light in - to the dark - ness, come,_____ Lord,

set ev - 'ry pri - so - ner free;_____ you_____
set ev - 'ry pri - so - ner free;_____ come,_____

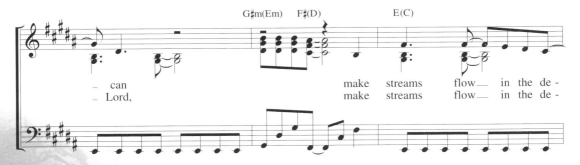

_____ can make streams flow_____ in the de -
_____ Lord, make streams flow_____ in the de -

Copyright © 2003 Thankyou Music/Adm. by worshiptogether.com Songs excl. UK & Europe,
adm. by Kingswaysongs, a division of David C Cook tym@kingsway.co.uk Used by Permission

we will be your hands and feet to - day, to - day.

**Coda**

let your king - dom come. let your king - dom

_ come. let your king - dom come.

# We are your people

We are your people, we live to serve you
with our different gifts and abilities.

We are your people, we live to serve you
from our different backgrounds and experiences.

We are your people, we live to serve you
with our different ages and needs.

We are your people, we live to serve you,
each of us called, each of us willing.

We are your people, we live to serve you.

*© Nick Harding*

297

# You dwell in the songs that we are singing
## (Restless)

Key=B

Audrey Assad
& Matt Maher

Capo 4(G)

Steadily ♩ = 67

Copyright © 2010 River Oaks Music Company (BMI)Matt Maher Publishing Designee
(Admin. by EMI CMG Publishing)Used by Permission

Therefore my **heart** is *glad* and my **tongue** *rejoices;* my **body** also will *live in hope*

*Acts 2:26*

# 96

# You knew me at the start
## (Jesus loves me)

Key=E

Gently, with feeling

Pete James

1. You knew me at the start,____
2. This is the life you made,____ and

you know me at____ the end;
jour-neyed with all____ the way;

dreams and re-a - li-ty,____ and ev-'ry-thing in____ be-tween.____
dreams and re-a - li-ty; and ev-'ry-thing in____ be-tween.____

**%. Chorus**

Je - sus loves me, this I know____ for sure;____

Copyright © 2011 Song Solutions Daybreak
www.songsolutions.org Used by Permission

oh, how he loves— me, this I know— for sure.—

# 97

# You never give up on us

Key=G

Chris Morton, James Gregory & Zac Robb

Steadily ♩ = 88

You ne-ver give up on us, Lord, you ne-ver let go

or turn a-way; we're hold-ing on to you, our God

is strong, our God is good.

1. You're the God of sal-va-tion, we call on your
2. You're the God of com-pas-sion, the friend of the

Copyright © 2011 Thankyou Music/Adm. by worshiptogether.com Songs excl. UK & Europe, adm. by kingswaysongs.com, a division of David C Cook tym@kingsway.co.uk Used by Permission.

This one sounds great on the acoustic CD of "Fresh New Songs for the Church"!

# 98. You say to us, "Seek my face"
## (One thirst and hunger)

Key=B

Jeremy Riddle

Capo 4(G)
Steadily; building

1. You say to us, 'Seek my face'; our hearts re-ply, 'Your face we

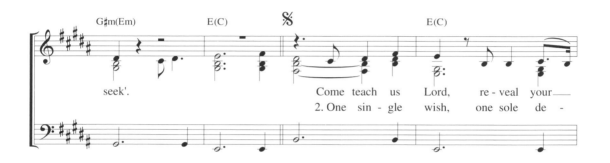

seek'. Come teach us Lord, re-veal your
2. One sin-gle wish, one sole de-

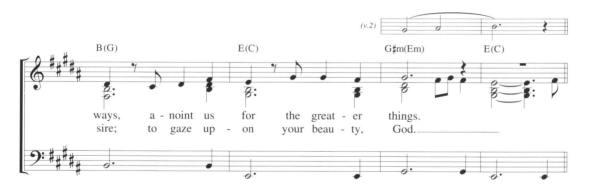

ways, a-noint us for the great-er things.
sire; to gaze up-on your beau-ty, God.

**Chorus**

We have ga-thered with one thirst and hun-ger, here to lift up

Copyright © 2011 Mercy/Vineyard Publishing/Admin by Song Solutions CopyCare
www.songsolutions.org Used by Permission

SPRING HARVEST

# WHERE THE WHOLE CHURCH COMES TOGETHER

For over thirty years Spring Harvest has been bringing the whole church together to worship, learn and grow.

Take a week to encounter God, be changed by that encounter and go out and change the world.

Find out more
www.springharvest.org

Memralife Group is a registered charity.

# 99

## Your love has opened my eyes
### (New day)

Key=B

Capo 4(G)

Ben Cantelon
& Nick Herbert

Driving

1. Your love has o-pened my eyes, in you I have come a-
live, a new day has come.

Your grace has turned me a - round, set my
(2.)We'll sing it loud, sing it strong, tell - ing

feet on so - lid ground, a new day has come.
of the Fa - ther's love we'll shine for you.

Copyright © 2010 Thankyou Music/Adm. by worshiptogether.com Songs excl. UK & Europe, adm. by kingswaysongs.com,
a division of David C Cook tym@kingsway.co.uk Used by Permission.

311

# 100

# Your love shines through space and time
## (Fill me)

Capo 2(G)

Steadily ♩ = 82

Key=A

Pete James

**Verse**

1. Your love___ shines ___ through space and___ time,
   clouds ___ up - on the___ wind,

and pier - ces___ through ___ the win - dow___ to
and fall like___ rain ___ on bar - ren___ plains;

the in - ner part of me, where deep cries out to deep, where
and let my life a - wake to you, like flow'rs in spring, my

mor - tal soul and hea - ven meet. Fill___ me, let my cup o-
heart and soul for - e - ver sing.

**Chorus**

- ver-flow;___ fill me, more than this life___ has known.___ Fill___

Copyright © 2011 Song Solutions Daybreak
www.songsolutions.org Used by Permission

# Chord Bridges to D

# Chord Bridges to E

**From G**

**From A**

**From C**

**From D**

# Chord Bridges to F

# Guitar Chord Charts

A good chord vocabulary is essential for a guitarist to feel confident when playing in worship, especially when the situation may involve reading a previously unseen piece of music or picking up a song quickly by ear. The chords on these pages are arranged in 'families' according to key. This is a beneficial way of remembering chords as most songs stick to these groupings. For each key, the first row shows the simplest form of each chord and the second line gives a more interesting substitution. The third line shows the chords most commonly used by guitarists derived by keeping some sort of pedal tone ringing in each chord and the fourth line shows inverted chords with an alternate bass note.

Also included are the Roman Numerals and Nashville Numbers associated with each chord. If you've not come across these before, they are simply an easy way of numbering each chord within a key. This is useful as it means you can take any chord progression in one key and instantly transpose it to another. Furthermore you can try out any of the chords in each column that corresponds to the relevant Roman Numeral and see if there is chord type or inversion which still fits but adds a different flavour. Experimentation like this may open up creative chord progressions that serve as a catalyst to help you to worship in fresh ways or to write new songs.

| Roman | I | II | III | IV | V | VI | VII |
|---|---|---|---|---|---|---|---|
| Nashville | 1 | 2 | 3 | 4 | 5 | 6 | 7 |
| 3-note chord (triad) | C | Dm | Em | F | G | Am | Bdim |
| 4-note chord | C maj7 | D m7 | E m7 | F maj7 | G7 | A m7 | B m7♭5 |
| Alternative substitute | C | D7sus4 | E m7 | F sus2 | G5 | A m7 | Dsus4/B |
| Alternative bass note | C/E | Dm/F | Em/G | F/A | F/G | Am/E | |

For all chords in the key of C# or Db, use the chords from the key of C with capo 1

**Key of C**

| Roman | I | II | III | IV | V | VI | VII |
|---|---|---|---|---|---|---|---|
| Nashville | 1 | 2 | 3 | 4 | 5 | 6 | 7 |

**Key of D**

| | I | II | III | IV | V | VI | VII |
|---|---|---|---|---|---|---|---|
| 3-note chord (triad) | D | Em | F#m | G | A | Bm | C#dim |
| 4-note chord | D maj7 | E m7 | F#m7 | G maj7 | A 7 | B m7 | C#m7♭5 |
| Alternative substitute | D sus2 | E m9 | F#m7 | G 6sus2 | A 7sus4 | B m11 | A add9/C# |
| Alternative bass note | D/F# | E m/B | F#m/A | G/B | G/A | Bm/F# | |

For all chords in the key of D# or E♭, use the chords from the key of D with capo 1

**Key of E**

| | I | II | III | IV | V | VI | VII |
|---|---|---|---|---|---|---|---|
| 3-note chord (triad) | E | F#m | G#m | A | B | C#m | D#dim |
| 4-note chord | E maj7 | F#m7 | G#m7 | A maj7 | B 7 | C#m7 | D#m7♭5 |
| Alternative substitute | E 5 | F#m11 | G#madd♭6 | A add9 | B add4 | C#m7 | D#alt |
| Alternative bass note | E/G# | F#m/C# | G#m/D# | A/C# | A/B | C#m/G# | |

For all chords in the key of F, use the chords from the key of E with capo 1

For all chords in the key of F# or Gb, use the chords from the key of E with capo 2

| Roman | I | II | III | IV | V | VI | VII |
|---|---|---|---|---|---|---|---|
| Nashville | 1 | 2 | 3 | 4 | 5 | 6 | 7 |

**Key of G**

| | I | II | III | IV | V | VI | VII |
|---|---|---|---|---|---|---|---|
| 3-note chord (triad) | G | Am | Bm | C | D | Em | F#dim |
| 4-note chord | Gmaj7 | Am7 | Bm7 | Cmaj7 | D7 | Em7 | F#m7♭5 |
| Alternative substitute | G | A7sus4 | Dsus4/B | Cadd9 | Dsus4 | Em7 | G/F# |
| Alternative bass note | G/D | Am/C | Bm/D | C/G | C/D | Em/G | |

For all chords in the key of G# or A♭, use the chords from the key of G with capo 1

**Key of A**

| | I | II | III | IV | V | VI | VII |
|---|---|---|---|---|---|---|---|
| 3-note chord (Triad) | A | Bm | C#m | D | E | F#m | G#dim |
| 4-note chord | Amaj7 | Bm7 | C#m7 | Dmaj7 | E7 | F#m7 | G#m7♭5 |
| Alternative substitute | Asus2 | Bsus4 | C#m7 | D6sus2 | Eadd9 | F#m11 | Eadd9/G# |
| Alternative bass note | A/E | Bm/F# | C#m/E | D/A | D/E | F#m/A | |

For all chords in the key of A# or Bb, use the chords from the key of A with capo 1

For all chords in the key of B, use the chords from the key of A with capo 2

# Thematic Index

## Call to Worship

All you nations clap your hands
As we gather together
Come and join the singing
Come on, my soul
Hope is here
Let our praise be
Let our praise be your welcome
Let the people say
We have come to worship
We've come here to gather

## Church, the People of God

All you nations clap your hands
As we gather together
Be merciful
Jesus, at the center of it all
Let our praise be
Lord, come build your glorious Church
Now may the peace of the Lord
On that day, there will be no injustice
Stand up, come on, stand your ground
There's a dance
We'll live as you have called us
We're in this battle together

## Come Lord Jesus: The Presence of God

Christ be in my waking
Come breathe on us now
Form us
God, you are my God
I will exalt you
Into your arms
Jesus, at the center of it all
Let our praise be
Spirit come
The broken, have come to the Mender
There is no love
We call to you, the living God
You can shine light into the darkness
You dwell in the songs that we
are singing
You say to us, "Seek my face"

## Communion

(SEE ALSO JESUS - CROSS AND
RESURRECTION)

History split by sacrifice
I look to the cross where my hope
is found
O precious sight
O, the blood

## Confession

All the poor and powerless
How great is your love
I'm standing at the cross
Into your arms
Lord, I come, I confess
O, the blood
You never give up on us

## Creation

At your name
Before the world was made
In the beginning
The perfect wisdom of our God
Who made the ground that I stand on

## Dedication and Commitment

Before the world was made
Break our hearts
Here I am
I look to the cross where my hope
is found
If my heart is overwhelmed
I'm bringing my sound
Jesus, at the center of it all
O precious sight
On that day, there will be no injustice
Our hearts will not forget
Take these hands
There is no love
Undivided love

## Faith and Trust

Before the world
Bless the Lord, O my soul
I will exalt you
If my heart is overwhelmed
On that day, there will be no injustice
Our hearts will not forget
Standing on this mountain top
The Lord is here among us
We're in this battle together
You can shine light into the darkness
You dwell in the songs that we
are singing
You never give up on us

## Family Worship

If God had a mobile phone
Jesus, at the center of it all
Let the people say
We have come to worship
When the sun is shining
Who made the ground that I stand on

## God, Lord and Father

Be lifted high
I'm standing at the cross
Into your arms
Lord, my life is an empty cup
Lord, come build your glorious Church
Nothing can tear us
Now may the peace of the Lord
Standing on this mountain top
The broken, have come to the Mender
What heart could hold the weight of
your love?
You knew me at the start
Your love has opened my eyes

## God's Love and Faithfulness

And can it be?
Before the world
God is able
God so loved, loved this world
Great is your love
Higher than the mountains that I face
History split by sacrifice
How great is your love
I want to scream it out
If I searched the heavens
If my heart is overwhelmed
Like a shelter
Nothing can tear us
O the deep, deep love of Jesus
O, the blood
Standing on this mountain top
The Lord is here among us
There is no love
What heart could hold the weight of
your love?
What love is this that always gives
Worship God with the morning
sunrise
You are a refuge
You knew me at the start
You never give up on us
Your love shines through space
and time

## Guidance and Direction

Christ be in my waking
Here I am
If God had a mobile phone
Lord, I come, I confess
Spirit come
The perfect wisdom of our God
What love is this that always gives
You dwell in the songs that we
are singing
You knew me at the start
Your love has opened my eyes

## Healing

As I go
Hope is here
If I searched the heavens
Into a world so bruised by sin
The broken, have come to the Mender
We call to you, the living God
You can shine light into the darkness
Your love has opened my eyes

## Heart Worship

As we gather together
Bless the Lord, O my soul
God, you are my God
Hallelujah, rejoice
Hope fills my soul
Hosanna in the highest
I want to scream it out
I will exalt you
I'm bringing my sound
It is by grace that we are saved
Let me wait in the majesty
Lord, my life is an empty cup

Nothing can tear us
Our hearts will not forget
Take these hands
The Lord is here among us
There is no love
We call to you, the living God
We have come to worship
We've come here to gather
What heart could hold the weight of your love?
When I stand before your throne
Worship God with the morning sunrise
You say to us, "Seek my face"
Your love has opened my eyes

## Heaven and the Promise of Eternity

Bless the Lord, O my soul
God, you are my God
Lord, come build your glorious Church
O the deep, deep love of Jesus
On that day, there will be no injustice
We're in this battle together
When I stand before your throne

## Holy Spirit

Come breathe on us now
In the beginning
Let our praise be
Let our praise be your welcome
Rise up
Spirit come
Your love shines through space and time

## Jesus - Cross and Resurrection

And can it be?
God is able
Great is your love
History split by sacrifice
Into a world so bruised by sin
Jesus, at the center of it all
O precious sight
We have heard a joyful sound
We were once in darkness
We're the forgiven
Who is like the Lord our God?

## Justice

Break our hearts
Form us
Lord, you hear the cry
May the life that flows from you flow in me
On that day, there will be no injustice
Our hearts will not forget
Stand up, come on, stand your ground
We'll live as you have called us
You are a refuge

## Love and Devotion

Christ be in my waking
God, you are my God
Hallelujah, rejoice
I will exalt you
If my heart is overwhelmed
I'm bringing my sound
Into your arms
Let me wait in the majesty
Let our praise be your welcome
Lord, my life is an empty cup
There is no love
Undivided love
We call to you, the living God
We have come to worship
We're the forgiven
Worship God with the morning sunrise

## Mercy, Grace and Forgiveness

And can it be?
Form us
God so loved, loved this world
History split by sacrifice
Hope is here
How great is your love
How strong did darkness appear
I'm standing at the cross
Into a world so bruised by sin
It is by grace that we are saved
Let the people say
Lord, I come, I confess
Lord, come build your glorious Church
Lord, you hear the cry
O precious sight
O, the blood
Rise up
This is the dream
Undivided love
We were once in darkness
We're the forgiven
What love is this that always gives
Who is like the Lord our God?
You never give up on us
Your love has opened my eyes

## Mission

All the poor and powerless
Be merciful
God so loved, loved this world
Hope is here
Like a shelter
May the life that flows from you flow in me
Our hearts will not forget
There's a dance
This is the dream
We have heard a joyful sound
We were once in darkness
You are a refuge
Your love has opened my eyes

## Mystery/Transcendence and Power Of God

At your name
God is able
If I searched the heavens
Into a world so bruised by sin
Let me wait in the majesty
O precious sight
Only one name
The heavens, horizons of this earth
The perfect wisdom of our God
What heart could hold the weight of your love?
Who is like the Lord our God?
Who made the ground that I stand on
Worship God with the morning sunrise
You can shine light into the darkness

## Praise and Thanksgiving

All you nations clap your hands
At your name
Come breathe on us now
God so loved, loved this world
Hosanna in the highest
How great is your love
How strong did darkness appear
I want to scream it out
Into a world so bruised by sin
Let our praise be
Let the people say
Oh the Lord, our strength and song
On that day, there will be no injustice
Our God is stronger
Standing on this mountain top
There's a dance
We have come to worship
We have heard a joyful sound
We'll live as you have called us
We've come here to gather
Who is like the Lord our God?
Worship God with the morning sunrise
You dwell in the songs that we are singing
Your love has opened my eyes

## Prayer and Intercession

God, you are my God
Jesus, at the center of it all
Lord, you hear the cry
Stand up, come on, stand your ground
We call to you, the living God
You say to us, "Seek my face"

## Proclamation

All the poor and powerless
At your name
Be lifted high
Before the world was made
Come and join the singing
Hope is here

Let our praise be
Let our praise be your welcome
Let the people say
Oh, the Lord, our strength and song
Only one name
Our God is stronger
Stand up, come on, stand your ground
The heavens, horizons of this earth
We have come to worship
We have heard a joyful sound
What heart could hold the weight of
your love?
Who is like the Lord our God?
You can shine light into the darkness
You never give up on us

## Renewal and Refreshment

Christ be in my waking
Come breathe on us now
Come on, my soul
Hallelujah, rejoice
Hope fills my soul
If my heart is overwhelmed
I'm standing at the cross
In the beginning
Into your arms
Lord, I come, I confess
Lord, my life is an empty cup
Nothing can tear us
Now may the peace of the Lord
Spirit come
The broken, have come to the Mender
The Lord is here among us
We call to you, the living God
You are a refuge
You dwell in the songs that we
are singing
Your love shines through space
and time

## Response

All the poor and powerless
And can it be?
Be lifted high
Before the world was made
Break our hearts

Form us
God, you are my God
Here I am
History split by sacrifice
Hosanna in the highest
How strong did darkness appear
I will exalt you
I'm bringing my sound
I'm standing at the cross
It is by grace that we are saved
Lord, my life is an empty cup
Lord, you hear the cry
May the life that flows from you flow
in me
Now may the peace of the Lord
O precious sight
On that day, there will be no injustice
Our hearts will not forget
Standing on this mountain top
Take these hands
The broken, have come to the Mender
There is no love
Undivided love
We were once in darkness
We'll live as you have called us
You are a refuge
You say to us, "Seek my face"
Your love shines through space
and time

## Spiritual Warfare

At your name
God is able
Great is your love
Hallelujah, rejoice
How strong did darkness appear
Like a shelter
Oh, the Lord, our strength and song
Only one name
Our God is stronger
Stand up, come on, stand your ground
This is the dream
We're in this battle together
You can shine light into the darkness

## Suffering and Trials

All the poor and powerless
Before the world
Christ be in my waking
God is able
Higher than the mountains that I face
If my heart is overwhelmed
Lord, my life is an empty cup
Lord, you hear the cry
Oh, the Lord, our strength and song
Stand up, come on, stand your ground
Standing on this mountain top
The broken, have come to the Mender
The Lord is here among us
The perfect wisdom of our God
We call to you, the living God
We have heard a joyful sound
What love is this that always gives
When I stand before your throne
You are a refuge
You can shine light into the darkness

## Suitable for Solo or Presentation

As I go
I'm standing at the cross
Lord, my life is an empty cup
Lord, you hear the cry
Now may the peace of the Lord
O precious sight
When I stand before your throne
You are a refuge
You knew me at the start

## Trinity

Holy Father rich in mercy
There's a dance

# Liturgy & Spoken Worship Index

# Musician's Notes: